Body Confidence

Body Confidence

Astrid Longhurst

MICHAEL JOSEPH
an imprint of
PENGUIN BOOKS

MICHAEL JOSEPH

Published by the Penguin Group
Penguin Books Ltd, 80 Strand, London wc2r orl, England
Penguin Putnam Inc., 375 Hudson Street, New York, New York 10014, USA
Penguin Books Australia Ltd, 250 Camberwell Road, Camberwell, Victoria 3124, Australia
Penguin Books Canada Ltd, 10 Alcorn Avenue, Toronto, Ontario, Canada m4v 3b2
Penguin Books India (P) Ltd, 11 Community Centre, Panchsheel Park, New Delhi – 110 017, India
Penguin Books (NZ) Ltd, Cnr Rosedale and Airborne Roads, Albany, Auckland, New Zealand
Penguin Books (South Africa) (Pty) Ltd, 24 Sturdee Avenue, Rosebank 2196, South Africa

Penguin Books Ltd, Registered Offices: 80 Strand, London wc2r orl, England

www.penguin.com

First published 2003
1

Set in 11.75/14.75 pt Monotype Minion
Typeset by Rowland Phototypesetting Ltd, Bury St Edmunds, Suffolk
Printed in England by Clays Ltd, St Ives plc

A CIP catalogue record for this book is available from the British Library

isbn 0–718–14592–5

This book is dedicated to:

Loz, Lynn, Katey, Barbie and my beautiful sister, Helen

Loz My music mystic diva – your beauty runs deep, your wisdom, eternal. Without you, this book would not have been written.

Lynn My dancing soul mate – our lives run in parallel, our laughter fuels our journeys. Shall I take 'forty'? You're the best!

Katey My beautiful soul sister – memories, moments and milestones of magic. I love the art you bring to my life.

Barbie My lovely 'Posy'. I love the bond we share – unique, powerful and deeply loving. Thank you for being so beautiful.

Helen My timeless moon babe, you shine brighter than any star, as you sparkle your own shimmering blend of 'wolf' magic. Go get it girl!

To all of you – I love you and thank you for being guiding lights on my own body journey.

Acknowledgements

My heartfelt thanks go to my agent Darley Anderson who had confidence in *Body Confidence* and gave the book a loving nudge in the right direction. Your enthusiasm was infectious – your support and belief, uplifting!

Thanks also go to Kerith Biggs and Lucie Whitehouse at the agency, whose professionalism and enthusiasm propelled the book happily along. Thank you both for all your hard work and support. Thanks also to Julia Churchill for everything you have done to help make this such a smooth process. I appreciate all your hard work – thank you.

Special thanks go to Louise Moore at Penguin, who allowed the book to fly and set my words free. Your vision, belief and excitement were inspiring – your energy, motivating! Special thanks also to Chantal Gibbs for your superb editorial skills, inspiration, support and sense of fun. Thank you also to Harriet Evans and the team at Penguin for every second of energy you put into the book. Many thanks also to Fiona Brown for her meticulous editing, helpful suggestions and fine-tuning. Thanks, too, to Keith Taylor for his expertise, care and energy.

I thank Barbie and Chris for 'being there' and my mum for 'being there' in spirit. Your energy lives on!

Thanks to all my dear friends, especially Loz, Lynn and Katey and all the wonderful people who have shared their stories with me and allowed me to include them here in this book. (All clients' names have been changed.)

Thanks to Helen and Tannii for being such a loving and fulfilling part of my life. I love you both. Helen – you saw beyond the angry, hurt, tormented and frustrated sister of your childhood and loved me anyway – thank you for your beauty and compassion.

Lastly, thanks to all the very special people I have been privileged to meet throughout my life, both past and present. Thank you for helping, teaching and guiding me through my own body journey.

The Publishers wish to thank the following copyright holders for permission to quote copyrighted material:

BUPA 'Amazing' campaign advertisement. Reprinted by permission of BUPA.

Article by Allen Corr. Reprinted by permission of the *RTE Guide*.

The Velveteen Rabbit by Margery Williams (Puffin, 1995).

Stop the Insanity by Susan Powter. Reprinted by permission of The Orion Publishing Group Ltd.

Unconditional Life by Deepak Chopra. Reprinted by permission of Bantam Books.

Awareness by Anthony De Mello. Reprinted by permission of Bantam Doubleday Dell Publishing Group, Inc.

Developing Gestalt Counselling by Jennifer MacKewn. Copyright © Jennifer MacKewn, 1997. Reprinted by permission of Sage Publications Ltd.

Submitted excerpt from *A Return to Love* by Marianne Williamson. Copyright © 1992 by Marianne Williamson. Reprinted by permission of HarperCollins*Publishers*.

A Woman's Worth by Marianne Williamson (Rider, 1994).

Portions reprinted from *A Course in Miracles*. Copyright © 1975 by Foundation for Inner Peace, Inc. All non-credited chapter openings are from *A Course in Miracles*.

The Beauty Myth by Naomi Wolf, published by Chatto & Windus. Used by permission of the Random House Group Limited.

Unlimited Power by Anthony Robbins. Copyright © Robbins Research Institute, 1986. Reprinted by permission of Simon & Schuster.

Awaken the Giant Within by Anthony Robbins. Copyright © Anthony Robbins 1991. Reprinted by permission of Simon & Schuster.

Create Your Own Reality by Nancy Ashley, adapted with permission of Simon & Schuster Adult Publishing Group. Copyright © 1982 by Nancy Ashley.

Every effort has been made to trace or contact all copyright holders. The publishers will be pleased to make good any omissions or rectify any mistakes brought to their attention at the earliest opportunity.

Contents

Introduction

I was amazed when I was first asked to present a fitness slot on national television. Not just any old slot either, but the most coveted and sought after one on daytime TV! My first reaction (after agreeing, then jumping up and down in the air and shoving my hand into my mouth to stop myself from screaming with excitement) was to ask, 'Do they know I'm not a size 10?' to which the reply was, 'Yes, that's one of the reasons they'd love you to do it!'

It was an instant success and I received phone calls and letters saying how great it was to see a larger woman exercising and being so fit, healthy, happy and positive about her life.

WOW! I still find it amazing!

Up until recently, this would have been unthinkable, as the presenters were all reed slim – certainly no bigger than a size 12. Personally, it is such an affirmation to me that when you view your body and your self with respect, love and acceptance and have belief in who you are, then anything can happen. Your most longed-for dreams can come true! I had achieved my all-time dream and I did it at a size 20 when for most of my life I had been struggling to achieve it as a size 10!

I realized that it wasn't my size that was the issue, but my own attitude towards my size and my body. Once I stopped seeing my body in a hateful, limited and negative way and began to accept **me** (big or small), an incredible process of change began to take place within me as I became happier, freer and more confident!

The newspapers went mad, wanting the exclusive story of how someone can love herself and be confidently happy and radiant at a size 20! Magazines wanted to know the secret of this thing called 'Body Confidence' and how their readers could attain it. The BBC booked me to mobilize the nation into action on a huge health and fitness spectacular and my fitness video went to number four in the fitness charts! Not bad for someone who not that long ago couldn't get out of bed because she felt so dreadful about herself!

My own self-hatred manifested itself through an eating disorder – bulimia (which at that time few people had even heard about!). I hated the way I looked, the way I felt, the way I was and who I was! I didn't value or care about me and spent most of the first part of my life wishing I could be someone else! My confidence levels dropped lower and lower along with my self-esteem and eventually, I only really felt safe if I was indoors and out of the way.

Learning how to love and have confidence in my body opened up huge pathways of adventure, love and fulfilment as I realized that I was stronger working **with** my body than against it. I stopped fighting the 'body wars' and took a different approach, by going straight to the point of conflict and working from the inside out! The war ceased to exist as I put myself in a 'win–win' position and knew that with my body on my side I could achieve anything.

My career, since encouraging people to jump off their sofas and bounce up and down at some ridiculous time in the morning, has been in Body Image Therapy. After qualifying as a psychotherapist I specialized in motivational counselling and all types of body confidence issues from low self-esteem to eating distress conditions.

It is incredible how having a positive and self-valuing attitude towards your body can dramatically change your life. Life is too short to spend it disliking the person you are. All too soon it's over, and you don't get another chance to live the life you've always dreamed of. Let's not waste the time we have by pulling our bodies apart, hating our thighs, criticizing our stomachs, and moaning that our bums are too big, our noses too small or our freckles too many!

Instead, let's go on a fantastic journey into the world of *Body Confidence* as we learn how to love our bodies, listen to the unique messages they give us and harness our power to transform our lives. Ultimately, when you feel confident about your body, you feel confident about yourself. Our bodies are where we live – our homes on this earth. Every single thing we do, think, feel, say or believe is experienced through our bodies. When that body is loved and valued, the experience is heightened and anything is possible. There is an intense feeling of inner joy and peace, which comes from truly just being **you!**

Having confidence in you and your body will lay the foundations for a happy and harmonious life with your body as your best friend. You know that you are safe in your 'home' and that feeling creates a sense of well-being and calmness. *Body Confidence* is the power behind the person.

Part One of this book will show you **why** *Body Confidence* can change your life. I share my own body story along with those of my clients, and my wish is that all of our stories and experiences will motivate you to take the first step on your own Body Journey. Part Two tells you **how** to do it – as you travel through a step-by-step process, which takes you on a magical mystery tour in the form of a mythological journey! Your own imagination, senses and creativity are evoked as you discover the Lost Village of Self-Belief, climb the 'mountain of self-esteem' and swim with dolphins at Here and Now Island. You will learn how to unlock your dreams and discover the key words, symbols and choices which will leave you feeling powerfully confident in a body you love.

So, here it is – the book – *Body Confidence*. It is for everyone – large, small, tall, thin, old and young. *Body Confidence* has nothing to do with size, shape, age or beauty, but everything to do with attitude, choice and love!

Whether you wish to change, heal, understand or just feel at home in your body, *Body Confidence* is your constant companion as you travel through your life. You cannot help but love your body after reading this book and if I can do it, anyone can!

Good luck, have fun and remember – loving your body is only a thought away!

Part One

Loving your body is only a **thought** away

1.

Home Alone

Do not go where the path may lead,
Go instead where there is no path and leave a trail.
Ralph Waldo Emerson

Our bodies are where we live, our physical homes throughout this lifetime. We experience our lives through our bodies. Everything we do, feel, think, say or believe is felt in our bodies, linked to our minds and filtered through to our spirits. We are fantastic, amazing human beings and yet our bodies have become a forgotten land, a place where few really want to visit and those who do never spend long enough there to really get to know the terrain. Imagine a home which is constantly being broken into and ransacked – nothing feels safe there any more and a part of you wishes you could move away to somewhere safer and more secure. For many people, having a negative body image and low body confidence can be likened to that home – you live there but there is a sense of insecurity around you. You may build up barriers to protect your 'home' or try to change certain parts of it to make it feel safer or more protected but sooner or later the paintwork begins to peel away and the walls start to crack. The same happens with us. We can lose weight, enlarge our breasts, liposculpt our thighs, tuck our tummies and lift our faces, but, ultimately, if we don't actually like the person we are then all of this is just a veneer and sooner or later the discontentment creeps back, luring us on to the next face-lift, boob job or diet trend. Our bodies have become a dumping ground for all our unfulfilled dreams, frustrations and doubts. We can blame our bodies for our lack of success, failed relationships or unhappy lives. We have lost confidence in our bodies and, subsequently, in who we are. Have you ever found yourself thinking that you wouldn't do certain things because you are too big, too short, not pretty enough, too tall, not athletic enough or just not the right image? Or maybe you thought that your life would be perfect and all your troubles would vanish if you just lost some weight. Have you ever put your life on hold while you waited for that elusive perfect time when you had lost the weight or flattened your stomach and finally all your dreams would come true? If you have, then you may lack body confidence. There are times when we all feel insecure about how we look but it is when we begin to see our bodies negatively on a daily basis that the problem really starts to have a negative impact on our lives.

Having body confidence is about making your body a safe place to be – somewhere that you always feel secure, happy and loved. You know that no matter what happens outside your 'home' you will always find a sense of strength within, just by being you and by being confident in who you are. You honour your beliefs, you act on your dreams and you experience life fully through a body that is cared for, appreciated and loved. In essence, it is the difference between really being here in your life, participating and feeling on every level, or watching the world go by from behind a misted glass window – you know this is your life but somehow you feel separate from it.

Clearing that glass window and focusing on my body in a positive light was a dramatic and exciting turn-around for me and suddenly my body became my best friend instead of my sworn enemy. With my body on my side I realized that I could do and achieve anything I wanted and began to see my dreams as actually happening instead of just staying locked up in my mind. The biggest change was that I was no longer fighting with myself and, as such, could now approach my life on a win–win basis.

I'll never forget the day it hit me that I was finally living the dream I had fantasized about since childhood. I can picture the scene right now . . . I was standing on stage at the London Coliseum with the English National Ballet behind me. I had been asked by GMTV to choreograph and present a funky ballet workout to a rock version of *The Nutcracker*. It was as we finished the piece with our feet closed in the fifth position and our arms held high above our heads that I realized what I was doing. Here I was, dancing on television with the English National Ballet, presenting my own slot on one of television's most popular morning shows and all of this at a size 20! I was doing all the things I had only dreamed about. Ten years ago I didn't want to get out of bed or be seen because I wasn't a model size 10. I hated my body with a vengeance and my self-esteem was non-existent. Had I been asked to present my workouts on national television at that stage in my life I would have said no. I would never have had the confidence or self-belief to appear on TV – it was hard enough just walking down the street! I would have missed the amazing opportunity to fulfil my innermost dreams because I lacked body confidence.

I believe that having confidence in your body and, subsequently, in how you see yourself will affect your life in a profound and dramatic way. Life is far too short to be spent in self-loathing, rejecting the person you are and the body you have. The minutes are ticking by as we worry about all of our shortcomings instead of celebrating our most positive strengths and abilities. I never used to notice how beautiful the day was because I was too busy noticing how ugly I thought I was. I was never fully in touch with my life because I was so out of touch with myself. When you deny and dislike the person you are then your entire world centres around this. I made excuses not to go to parties; I failed to show up to go swimming or horse riding. I backed out of going away on holiday with friends and later on in my twenties I found reasons not to get involved in relationships or have sex. The ridiculous thing was that underneath it all I desperately wanted to experience all those things but felt unworthy of allowing my body or myself that pleasure.

My Life Would be Perfect Except for my Fat Bum!

One of my clients exclaimed passionately the other day that her life really would be just perfect if it wasn't for her fat behind. This lady is attractive, funny and successful. She runs her own lingerie company, is adored by her family and friends, and has three strong, bright, healthy children and a husband who loves her very much. She has enough time to enjoy her own personal hobbies and interests and yet all she sees is a life that isn't so great because she feels her derrière is too large! Too large for whom? For her husband? For her children? For her family and friends or her colleagues? No, her husband thinks she is sexy and beautiful as she is. Her children love their mum to bits, and her friends, family and work colleagues wouldn't change her in any way. They can't understand what she is so unhappy about. The truth is, my client's image of her own body doesn't come up to the image of the perfect body which she has created in her own mind. To her, she will never be 'quite right' until she has wiped out the natural curves from her backside that she sees as huge mountains of excess fat. She wants to be able to enjoy her life and appreciate all that she has but feels a failure because she hasn't got a tiny backside. The sad thing is that she doesn't really feel good about the rest of her life because she is so disappointed in herself. Her confidence is beginning to suffer and she feels as if she isn't really living her life to the full. There is nothing else in her life that she can blame for her feelings of frustration and unfulfilment so she has done what so many of us do – blamed her body. By blaming her body, my client was actually saying, 'Look, you see, I don't have it all – I'm still one of you. Don't envy my success because I still suffer – I still have problems.' As we worked together we discovered that her negative body image is locked up in the guilt she feels in having so much good in her life. Her parents were extremely frugal and during her upbringing any luxury was kept to the barest minimum. In her mind if she feels bad about herself then she can't be envied, and this keeps her from really living in the moment, enjoying all that she has.

Another client blames her height (6 feet 1 inch) for her lack of success at work, and a good friend of mine blames her androgynous figure for her inability to sustain a long-lasting relationship. She refers to herself as 'a stick insect on legs' and will even smack or hit her breasts when she feels particularly down, saying that there's nothing there to feel anything anyway! It is not her shape that is causing her the relationship problems but how she refers to herself. She does not find herself attractive and therefore feels that no one else will find her attractive. Her self-image and self-worth are so low that she can't see the wonderful, warm and witty woman she is. Men are attracted to her bubbly and fun personality and yet her lack of confidence in her body means that she cannot understand how anyone will ever love her. Once again, her negative body image is getting in the way of her life and she too is looking at her life through that misted glass window.

Sex was Like Making Love on a Film Set

She reminds me of a relationship I had a long time ago when I was going out with a wonderful, caring man who thought the world of me. The problem was that I didn't think the world of myself and although he always said how much he adored me I would continually tell him that he would love me more when I was skinny. It caused arguments, as he genuinely did love me for who and how I was at that time, but I just couldn't believe him. He would put his arm around my waist and I would flinch. It wasn't that I didn't want him to touch me but that I thought he could feel the excess fat around my middle. He thought it was his fault that I didn't want him to touch me.

Making love with him was a pre-arranged affair – forget spontaneity or real passion – I was far too body conscious for that! I would only let him see the parts of my body that I **wanted** him to see and would always have a huge selection of different fabrics or sheets that I could drape over myself at any given time. Thus, making love became a bit like a scene on a film set. I wanted to be viewed perfectly by him and real passionate abandonment was out of the question. How could I let myself go when I was far too interested in maintaining the perfect image? I was far more interested in manoeuvring my body into the best-draped pose I could muster than in losing myself to the raptures of true delight. Forget orgasms, forget being lost in the moment and, ultimately, forget the relationship! We parted on good terms but there has always been a part of me that regrets not being able to really enjoy his love and believe in it. Looking back, I realize that I was far too full of body hate to be able to experience body love – either my own or his.

You Can Never be Too Thin, Too Rich or Too Beautiful to Suffer From Lack of Body Confidence

A few years ago, a good friend of mine dragged me along to a fast-paced aerobics class. I had been saying that I wanted to go and do someone else's class and she recommended this one. It was fantastic – the music pumped out its heavy dance club beat and as the music got faster I got hotter and hotter. My body felt electric as the instructor took us through a highly choreographed fitness routine. The instructor herself looked amazing. She was tall, lithe and finely muscled. Her long auburn hair was tied back to reveal an incredibly pretty face and she came across as caring and considerate to her class members. I remember it was thus a great shock when she told us how much she disliked her body when we were chatting after the class. I asked her what she felt was wrong with it. She lifted up her Lycra sports top to reveal a brown flat tummy.

'Look at all of that!' she said, pinching together a tiny amount of skin. We both leaned closer to try and see what she was showing us. 'And,' she went on, 'look at my thighs – far too big for my bone structure!' Again, we could see nothing wrong with them and said so. I asked her if she was **really** that unhappy with her body, to which she replied, 'Everyone thinks I look great and that I must really love my body because I teach fitness, and to them I don't have anything to worry about.' She took a long sigh and continued,

'The truth is that I don't feel very confident about my looks or me. I worry about every single extra pound and never feel truly satisfied with how I look.'

I was stunned – here was this pretty, fit, intelligent woman who disliked parts of her body to such an extent that she felt inadequate and embarrassed about a shape that many of us would love to have. To me, total fitness is about being healthy in your mind as well as your body, which is one of the reasons I went on to work with body image psychology.

What is happening when people are pushing their bodies to the height of physical fitness but can't appreciate themselves once they get there? What is the point of having super-sleek thighs or six-pack abs when you don't value your body and are still dissatisfied with how you look? When is enough enough?

The saying 'You can never be too rich or too thin' (coined by the Duchess of Windsor in the 1930s) is seriously flawed. Being a millionaire is no guarantee for feeling great about who you are or how you look and, as the UK now has nearly 3.5 million anorexics and bulimics, being too thin is a potential danger in itself.

Change 'It's Impossible' to 'I'm Possible!'

The truth is that *Body Confidence* has nothing to do with size, shape, beauty, age or plastic surgery to change those bits you dislike. You can change your entire shape to become the most beautiful, perfectly-honed body you can create, but it will never bring you joy or happiness if your mind is locked up in a negative body image or you are unable to appreciate what you have. I remember chatting to a male friend of mine who was dating a stunning model. He said that she was absolutely gorgeous but she could never see it. It made for a difficult relationship, as she was so insecure about her looks. His words really struck home when he said, 'Her body was this beautiful thing – she just never knew how to operate it!'

Our bodies can become the focus for how we really feel about **ourselves** and all too often we end up blaming our bodies for the things we have never achieved in our lives. We feel that if we lost 10 lb in weight or had a flat tummy, were taller, shorter, prettier or bustier, then our lives would be perfect. To us, our bodies have become the reason we don't succeed or we aren't happy. They are our ultimate distraction so that we don't have to look deeper into ourselves and realize that perhaps it **isn't** our bodies that are the problem, but our relationships/jobs/environments. The danger is that we may end up blaming anything which doesn't go right in our lives on a part (or the whole) of our bodies we consider not 'perfect'. This is crazy, as the vital truth is that first, we will never be 'perfect', and, secondly, it is our attitudes to our bodies and ourselves which ultimately shapes our lives.

Look at the actor, Danny De Vito. By today's so-called standards of perfection he probably doesn't score too highly in the hundred sexiest men list, and yet he oozes body and self-confidence. The reason we even know his name is because he got out there into the world and did what he loved doing – acting. He could have sat at home and thought, 'Hey, I'm not really leading man material – perhaps I won't bother – who would want to book me?' But he used his body and looks to work for him. On some level he accepted that he was never going to be 6 feet 2 and hunky, or have the boyish windswept looks of Brad Pitt – but he could use what he had and go with it. There is only one Brad Pitt – there is only one Danny De Vito. There is only one of **us** in existence in this universe – we too can use what we have and go with it, creating and shaping our lives minute by minute in a kind and loving way. We can see the strength in our bodies, feel the passion in our hearts and the warmth in our arms as we begin to embrace ourselves mind, body and spirit. You might not be as beautiful as Cindy Crawford or as slim as Victoria Beckham – you may not have the brain of Carol Vorderman or the voice of Christina Aguillera, but you are you – there is not another like you in the entire universe and that makes you unique! You are special just because you **are!**

Acceptance is the Key to Change

My clients often say to me that if they accept themselves they fear they will stop caring about the way they look and let themselves go completely. Accepting yourself doesn't mean that you care less about you – it means that you bring yourself, as you are right now, fully into this moment. It means that you look at your body, your face, your posture and the way you are. Instead of denying our bodies by not wanting to look at them, or by criticizing certain parts, we need to put ourselves in a position of power by beginning to 'own' our bodies. Once you actually have something you will be able to change it – how can you change something you never really had? In accepting you, you begin to look at you.

In looking at yourself you may find that you notice things you never noticed before. When you really look at someone deeply and with acceptance, a certain luminosity begins to shine through. The whole person becomes visible.

I Didn't Fail the Diet – the Diet Failed Me!

Maggie, a client of about three months, came bubbling into her session one afternoon and told me that she finally understood why she could never lose the weight she wanted. She realized, after years of putting herself down and making her own life a misery because she could never stick to a diet, that it wasn't her that was the failure – it was the diet. 'I always thought that I was no good because I could never stick to a diet longer than a few days – a week at the most,' she said enthusiastically, 'but I've realized that it's the diet that's wrong – I can't survive on cabbage soup, I hate eating before 9.00 am and I feel bloated up on pasta and potatoes!' I asked her what her answer was and she gave me a broad smile and said, 'I'm not going to go on any of those diets any more. No one knows my body better than me, so I'm going to work out my own eating plan based on what suits me and makes me feel good.'

She was true to her word. She researched the vitamin and mineral content of the foods she loved to eat and put together her own balanced eating 'idea'. She set it around her lifestyle and when she liked to eat and even began to enjoy trying out new recipes – just for fun! No foods were banned but she just made a mental note if she began to crave certain foods more than others. Was it the food she needed or a hug? A chat? Or was she just using food as a distraction from something she was putting off?

Over the months of working together, Maggie's self-acceptance allowed her to really start to know herself. She stopped trying to force her body into what it 'should' be and began to take notice of what it was. She knew her body rejected rigid diet plans and certain foods. She hated to eat early – it made her feel sick, so she began to have a fruit juice and a cup of tea and then eat a little later in the morning. She created her own balanced eating plan to fit her own unique lifestyle.

She began to drop a little weight and was thrilled with the changes she was making in her life. But as she said, the biggest change came from within – from accepting who she was, her body and the way she liked to do things. She stopped comparing her body to that of a supermodel and stopped asking her body to conform to someone else's idea of a diet. She began to cut out negative thoughts along with negative eating plans and built a new, kinder and happier image of herself. In accepting herself Maggie has found the key to change. Her weight loss was not the issue – it was just a by-product of Maggie listening to and loving herself enough to begin to accept what her true needs were and how she felt about herself. On our last session together she said that it was great that she had lost some weight but that it was no longer such a big deal. Amazing words from someone who told me three months earlier that her life was unbearable and that she couldn't see the point in carrying on at the size she was!

How Much are You Worth?

One of the most exciting things about changing your body and self-image is that it goes hand in hand with how you value yourself – your self-worth. Someone with a low or negative body image very often has feelings of low self-worth – of feeling valueless. Things we don't value are very often treated badly or discarded. We very often ignore the object we don't value and, like an unwanted gift, we may hide it away so that we don't have to look at it. Very often the decisions and the choices we make in our lives are based on how we feel and how much we value ourselves. A friend of mine recently went for a job interview for a position he knew he didn't really want. The one he wanted was paying quite a lot more money and had a good deal more responsibility to go with it. As we chatted over a cup of tea he explained that he just didn't feel 'up to' the higher-profile job. As we continued to talk I discovered that he held all the necessary qualifications and had been working in exactly the same environment for over ten years. In other words, he knew his business and was good at it and yet he refused to value what he had. He put himself down and undervalued his experience, training and managerial skills, which were excellent. When I gently pointed this out to him he simply shrugged, sighed and said, 'I guess I don't feel good enough – it's a lot more money and although I could really do with it I don't think I'm really worth that sort of income.'

What is happening here is that my friend only saw himself in a particular way within specific boundaries. Although he desperately wanted the new job he wouldn't allow himself even to go for the interview, as he was so sure that he would fail to be offered the position. Although his professional skills were high, his own self-worth was low which meant that no matter how talented or brilliant he may be in his career he would never really allow himself to truly shine.

Like my friend, so many of us don't actually realize how valuable we are and we perceive ourselves in a negative way – never seeing or appreciating our full potential.

The clues to how much you value yourself are there. Listen to what you say about yourself when you are talking to friends, family, work colleagues, etc. Do you speak about yourself in a positive or negative way? When someone pays you a compliment do you feel embarrassed? Do you shrug it off as nothing? Do you even hear it? Or do you smile and say 'thank you'? How do you refer to yourself? A friend of mine always says how stupid she is when anything goes wrong and another always begins every sentence with the word 'sorry'. It's as if she is apologizing for whatever she is about to say – 'Sorry, but I just wondered if . . .' 'Sorry, but I just thought that . . .' 'Sorry, but would you like me to . . .' You get the idea?

People often find compliments hard to accept and we sometimes never even hear the positive, lovely things that people say, as we are too busy listening to our own inner negative self-talk. Or, if we do hear it we undervalue ourselves by handing the compliment back. I remember once offending a friend of mine by doing just this. She had commented on my healthy-looking suntan after I had returned from holiday, to which I immediately replied, 'Well, the sun could hardly miss me could it?' My friend looked a little embarrassed and said, 'No, I didn't mean that, I just thought you looked very well.' In one sentence I showed my friend exactly what I thought of my body, rebuffed her compliment and made it a big issue. I could have just said, 'Thanks'.

Body Confidence is about developing that sense of self-worth. It's about allowing yourself to shine and not apologizing for who you are. It's about moving past your own boundaries – the walls that you build to keep you in or to keep others out. It's an inner knowing that you are more than a size, a shape, a look or an ability. These things do not define or confine you unless you allow it. It's always your choice. For instance, it's a fact that I am a size 20 but what else does that tell you? Nothing – it's just a fact. It's neither good nor bad – it is as it is. It doesn't tell you who I am or what I do, my likes or my dislikes, my joys or my sadness. It doesn't even give you a picture of what I look like. I remember taking part in a television chat show and the subject was 'Can Big Be Beautiful?' I was intro-duced for the first time to the producer, who looked slightly taken aback. As we shook hands she said that she hadn't expected me to look like I did – that she thought someone who was size 20 would be much bigger than I was. I laughed and asked her what she thought size 20 was supposed to look like and she stumbled over her words as she said, 'Well, er, um . . . fat.'

I think in that moment she answered her own show's question as she realized that big can be beautiful, big can be successful, big can be confident, big can be creative and multitalented . . . Big can also be the exact opposite of all of the above – it all depends on the image you have of yourself and the value you give to yourself.

Think of it this way; imagine yourself as a work of art. There is only one of you in this universe, you are unique. As a unique work of art we are priceless – our value is beyond comparisons with no limits. Having body confidence hinges on how you **choose** to see yourself. It's all about self-perception. If you see yourself as unattractive or are disappointed by the way you look, you create a mind-set that will do everything it can to create more disappointment and pain.

A model I once worked with was so confident about herself and portrayed such self-assurance that her boyfriend never really knew what size she was and would always buy her size 12 underwear. She laughed as she said, 'It almost seems a shame to tell him that I'm a size 16, but I would like to wear some of the stuff he buys me – so maybe I will!'

Body Hurt

Hurting our bodies is something we may begin to do when we lack body confidence. This may be to a greater or lesser degree, but how we perceive ourselves has a direct impact on how we live our lives. I hurt myself through food – either too much of it or none at all. Others may hurt themselves through drink, drugs, excessive working, rigid and punishing exercise regimes, allowing themselves to stay in abusive relationships, etc. All of these have a negative effect on the body and, in turn, the mind. Body hurt may be extreme or really quite mild in its manifestation. If you find that what you do is determined by how you feel about your body – you are compromising your life and self in a huge way. There is nothing that you can't do – every negative thought can be changed to a positive, exciting and powerful new set of beliefs. There is no reason in this world why you have to be limited by how you look or perceive yourself to look. Your body is you – a marvellous, unique work of art in continual process. Think of all the thousands of tiny miracles which take place in your body every day of your life. Every single thought is acted upon by your body – you move, run, stretch, yawn, laugh, walk, cry, make love, hug, hold, caress, work at your particular job/career, sleep; the list is endless and fantastic. So many of us take this incredible gift for granted, never allowing ourselves to see the true beauty each one of us has.

The sad truth is that your body knows when you hate it and suffers when you hurt it.

One of my clients is desperately trying to lose some weight. She is in her early sixties and has a job touring the country teaching arts and crafts to various groups. When I first met her she told me that she wanted to lose weight on her thighs, which she labelled as disgusting, revolting, huge and monstrous. I asked her to look at the adjectives she had used to describe her legs and notice the depth of negative feeling involved. She tried to get me to join her in her own low opinion of her legs and said, 'But they **are** gross aren't they – look at them!' Her legs were big, certainly, but they were in no way monstrous or disgusting or any of the other words she had used to describe them.

We looked at how else she could describe her legs and after some time she came up with the words strong, big, powerful, substantial and active. This was a huge shift in her perception of her body and as she said these words her eyes welled up with tears. Instead of using words full of emotional negative feeling she used words that described her legs in a positive and more accurate way. Although she did have big legs they certainly were not revolting – they were just big. It was her perception that made them revolting. It was an emotional session as she told me about a recent hip injury she had sustained and how she had been unable to walk for a few months. She had attended intensive physiotherapy sessions, which enabled her once again to walk unaided, and she remembered how wonderful that had felt. Her legs were still supporting her and allowing her to move from one place to another and enjoy her life. She loves to dance and the thought that she might not have been able to do this again had made her see and appreciate her legs in a new, more empowering light. The key issue here is that she was able to shift her focus from a negative, low emotional state into one in which she could perceive her body in a powerfully self-affirming way.

This is one of the key factors in *Body Confidence*. In taking away the self-abusive hateful words and replacing them with ones which appreciated her body, my client was able to release the pain she carried within her body. Her thighs had always been the reason why she never felt sexy, never wore jeans, never went swimming any more, and refused dates and social events. Much of her life had been put on hold and forgotten about as she blamed her legs for her missing out on life. I saw her recently and she was wearing jeans. She laughed as she exclaimed that this was the first time she had ever worn anything but a skirt in over sixty years! I asked her how it felt and her whole face lit up as she said, 'I feel like a teenager – a 63-year-old teenager!' She still wants to lose weight on her thighs but she is now doing it in a positive, kind and loving way. She has joined an aqua-aerobics class which she enjoys, and is treating her whole body with the respect and love she feels she deserves. I found myself welling up with emotion as she told me that for the first time in her life she feels special. Not for anything in particular that she has achieved but just because she is who she is. **This is a huge achievement!** Do not underestimate the power in what has occurred here. Anything can happen now – her whole life is now being lived on another level. Instead of dragging herself down she is lifting herself up and anything is possible! She is now open to new and exciting possibilities whereas before she missed out on so much because she was locked up in body shame and self-doubt.

Make Your Body Your Best Friend

The good news is that positive body image can be created and your body can become one of your most powerful allies. By learning to trust, like and connect with your body you can gain access to an entire new you. Your senses will become heightened as you begin to 'know' what it is your body (and self) desires at any time. As you begin to treat your body with a new-found respect, old addictive or self-hurting patterns may disappear completely. I discovered that by learning to actually have some respect for my body, my bulimic behaviour began to change and I slowly stopped bingeing. It wasn't as if I tried to stop, it was just a part of the natural process of beginning to like me. In liking me I began to care about me and suddenly I found that I didn't want to binge to the same extent as before. It happened slowly, over a period of time, but gradually I was aware that instead of bingeing every day it was happening every two days and then every week, every month and finally I just stopped altogether. No big deal – I just didn't want to hurt me any more.

Treat Your Body as You Would Your Lover

For the next week, imagine that you are going to treat your body as if it were your lover – someone you really care about and want the best for. Become aware of your body's needs and wishes and then try to make those wishes come true, no matter how small or inconsequential they may seem. Feed your body the food you would love to eat on a romantic evening out with your lover, buy yourself your favourite drink and enjoy it. Most importantly listen to what you say about you. If you find that you are putting yourself down or selling yourself short then stop and imagine what you would be saying to someone you loved who was doing this. What would be your response if your partner said things like, 'It's no use, I'm just no good at this,' or, 'I'm so fat/ugly/skinny and stupid,' or, 'I hate the way I look'? You would probably try and reassure them that they were okay and were not any of the things they were saying about themselves. You might take some time to listen to them and ask what was going on and why they were feeling like that. You would probably tell them that you loved them for who they are and try to help them build up their own positivity towards themselves. In short, you would gently affirm all of their most wonderful qualities and tell them not to be so hard on themselves. You wouldn't nod your head and say, 'Yes, I agree with you – you **are** stupid,' or, 'You're right, you are no good and I'm not surprised you hate the way you look – I hate it too!' (well, not unless perhaps this relationship was about to end!). However, it's very easy for us to say all those damaging words to ourselves and we never stop to counteract them – we believe them to be true about ourselves and constantly berate ourselves for falling short in some way, shape or form. Next time you catch yourself doing just that, stop, take a deep breath and imagine what you would say to someone you loved – then say it to yourself. Even if you don't believe it, still say it!

This kind of positive reaffirming self-talk is powerful and effective and one of the major tools for developing body and self-confidence. (See Chapter Three, Body Talk.)

How Much Body Confidence do You Have?

Your own body confidence will fluctuate and change subtly from day to day and in some cases even from hour to hour. These changes are normal and depend on a number of factors – your health, tiredness, job, people around you, family demands, etc. There are days when everyone, no matter how confident, will feel low or just not 'up for it'.

The difference is that someone with a higher level of body confidence will be able to recognize these days for what they are and know that these feelings will pass. They know that no matter what their day may bring they have the inner resources to adapt and cope with it. In other words they have a strong core of body and self-confidence. Like a tree in a storm, they may bend and sway with the elements but they stand strong in knowing who they are.

I have devised the Body Confidence Scale to give you some idea of how strong your own levels of body confidence are and how the image you have of your body affects your self-confidence and self-worth.

There are five different sections, all relating to your body. They are:

★ **Lifestyle**
★ **Body Care**
★ **Body/Self-Beliefs**
★ **Influences**
★ **The Sensual Body**

Answer each section by strongly agreeing, agreeing, disagreeing or strongly disagreeing with the statement.

SA   = Strongly Agree
A   = Agree
D   = Disagree
SD   = Strongly Disagree

Try not to spend too long thinking about your answers – go with your first thoughts or feelings. Then, turn to the Body Confidence Score Sheet and find the values given for each answer.

The Body Confidence Scale is NOT a judgement on who you are. It is intended to give you some insight into where you may be right now. It will highlight your stronger and weaker areas and give you clues to understanding the messages your body is giving you. Knowing who and where we are gives us the power to move from that point, and the Body Confidence Scale gently outlines which areas you may need to start with first.

Be as honest as you can in your answers. Remember, there is no right or wrong way to respond – it's all just about you.

Lifestyle

	SA	A	D	SD
1. I have a good social life	☐	☐	☑	☐
2. I have as many friends as the next person	☐	☐	☑	☐
3. I take time for myself during my day	☐	☑	☐	☐
4. My dream job/career will always remain just that – a dream	☐	☐	☐	☐
5. I welcome new opportunities and enjoy change	☐	☐	☐	☐
6. I tend to wear dark colours to camouflage my shape	☑	☐	☐	☐
7. I buy clothing that is too small as an incentive to succeed when dieting	☐	☐	☐	☐
8. I feel that I have been discriminated against because of the way I look, especially in the workplace or job interview environment	☐	☐	☐	☑
9. I might not be 'perfect' but I enjoy being me and value who I am	☑	☐	☐	☐
10. My body stops me from living the life that I want	☐	☑	☐	☐

Body Care

	SA	A	D	SD
1. I always make sure I get enough sleep	☑	☐	☐	☐
2. I regularly skip meals	☐	☐	☑	☐
3. I drink less than ten units of alcohol a week (One unit = a standard glass of wine)	☑	☐	☐	☐
4. I would consider plastic surgery	☐	☐	☐	☐
5. I tend to avoid beauty treatments where I need to strip off	☐	☑	☐	☐
6. The idea of joining a gym is just too scary for words	☑	☐	☐	☐
7. I feel that I don't treat my body with enough care – I'm surprised I'm still going!	☑	☐	☐	☐

8. I hardly do any exercise ☐ ☐ ☐ ☐
9. I always seem to be on some sort of diet ☐ ☐ ☐ ☐
10. I feel that changing my body is the answer to many of my problems ☐ ☐ ☐ ☐

Body/Self-Beliefs

	SA	A	D	SD
1. I wish I were more assertive	☐	☐	☐	☐
2. I feel that I am a person of worth, at least on an equal level with others	☐	☐	☐	☐
3. On the whole I am satisfied with myself	☐	☐	☐	☐
4. I feel self-conscious about my appearance	☐	☐	☐	☐
5. I take a positive attitude towards myself	☐	☐	☐	☐
6. I feel I do not have much to be proud of	☐	☐	☐	☐
7. I wish I could have more respect for myself	☐	☐	☐	☐
8. I feel that I have a number of good qualities	☐	☐	☐	☐
9. All in all, I am inclined to agree that I am a failure	☐	☐	☐	☐
10. On the whole I feel that life is a joyous experience – I live it well	☐	☐	☐	☐

Influences

	SA	A	D	SD
1. I think people judge me by the way I look	☐	☐	☐	☐
2. When I go shopping I always buy what my friends say I look best in	☐	☐	☐	☐
3. There are certain sports/activities which I won't take part in because of my shape or size	☐	☐	☐	☐
4. I perceive others to have a better life than me	☐	☐	☐	☐
5. After looking at pictures of glamorous models in magazines, I feel depressed	☐	☐	☐	☐
6. I tend to feel that what others say about me is right	☐	☐	☐	☐

7. The very thought of undressing in front of other people makes me squirm ☐ ☐ ☐ ☐

8. I feel that I do not match up when I compare myself to others ☐ ☐ ☐ ☐

9. I always feel I should apologize for how I look ☐ ☐ ☐ ☐

10. Other people's opinions are very important to me ☐ ☐ ☐ ☐

The Sensual Body

	SA	A	D	SD
1. I feel that I am sexually attractive	☐	☐	☐	☐
2. I am in tune with, and listen to my body's needs	☐	☐	☐	☐
3. I enjoy having sex with the lights left on	☐	☐	☐	☐
4. I am happy to look at my body naked	☐	☐	☐	☐
5. I never let my partner see me naked	☐	☐	☐	☐
6. I take time to relax during my week	☐	☐	☐	☐
7. When I make love I get lost in the moment	☐	☐	☐	☐
8. My body gives me much pleasure	☐	☐	☐	☐
9. I feel that lack of body confidence affects my sex life negatively	☐	☐	☐	☐
10. I don't really feel very sexual or sensual	☐	☐	☐	☐

Score Sheet

Match your answer from each question to the scores below. Then, for each section, add all ten scores together so you have a separate score for Lifestyle, Body Care, Body/Self-Beliefs, Influences and The Sensual Body. You will need to refer to each of these section scores later on to give you a more in-depth view of your lowest and highest areas of Body Confidence. Then, add the scores from each section together to give you an overall score for The Body Confidence Scale. Do not add the total score together until each section has been broken down.

Lifestyle

	SA	A	D	SD
1	4	3	2	1
2	4	3	2	1
3	4	3	2	1
4	1	2	3	4
5	4	3	2	1
6	1	2	3	4
7	1	2	3	4
8	1	2	3	4
9	4	3	2	1
10	1	2	3	4

Body Care

	SA	A	D	SD
1	4	3	2	1
2	1	2	3	4
3	4	3	2	1
4	1	2	3	4
5	1	2	3	4
6	1	2	3	4
7	1	2	3	4
8	1	2	3	4
9	1	2	3	4
10	1	2	3	4

Body/Self-Beliefs

	SA	A	D	SD
1	1	2	3	4
2	4	3	2	1
3	4	3	2	1
4	1	2	3	4
5	4	3	2	1
6	1	2	3	4
7	1	2	3	4
8	4	3	2	1
9	1	2	3	4
10	4	3	2	1

Influences

	SA	A	D	SD
1	1	2	3	4
2	1	2	3	4
3	1	2	3	4
4	1	2	3	4
5	1	2	3	4
6	1	2	3	4
7	1	2	3	4
8	1	2	3	4
9	1	2	3	4
10	1	2	3	4

The Sensual Body

	SA	A	D	SD
1	4	3	2	1
2	4	3	2	1
3	4	3	2	1
4	4	3	2	1
5	1	2	3	4
6	4	3	2	1
7	4	3	2	1
8	4	3	2	1
9	1	2	3	4
10	1	2	3	4

| 200 |
| 190 |
| 180 |
| 170 |
| 160 |
| 150 |
| 140 |
| 130 |
| 120 |
| 110 |
| 100 |
| 90 |
| 80 |
| 70 |
| 60 |
| 50 |
| 40 |
| 30 |
| 20 |
| 10 |
| 0 |

The Body
Confidence Scale

Where Are You on The Body Confidence Scale?

The Body Confidence Scale gives you an idea of areas that may need more confidence, love, support or attention. It is not an indicator of how good or bad your confidence levels may be and is certainly not intended to be judgemental or critical in any way. In terms of body confidence, how you view yourself has a direct result on how you treat yourself and this has an impact on every other area in your life. Confidence is something that changes daily, and it is the skills in staying positive, strong and focused on your goals which are of importance here.

Look at your overall score to determine where you are on the Body Confidence Scale. Afterwards, look at your individual section scores. These can highlight stronger and weaker areas and may help you to understand where you need to focus your attention and love the most.

Overall Scores

If you scored 55 or below
This score indicates areas of vast potential that are as yet untapped and unchallenged. You know that you have work to do to make you feel great about being you. Lack of body and self-confidence may be affecting your life on every level and you may be coming to the point where you are not going to take it any more. There is a saying that we change through either inspiration or desperation and perhaps the 'Journey' in Part Two of this book will inspire the changes you seek. You may be searching tentatively for your own answers and it may take time and lots

of love and kindness on your part to begin to unlock your own doors to total body confidence. The good news is that body confidence can be achieved and that everything you dream of feeling, being and doing can be realized.

The key is to travel gently, moving at your own pace in your own time. You will need great compassion, kindness and understanding towards yourself as you gradually begin to grow stronger and surer of you. Over time, you will find that an inner shift is taking place as you develop your trust, belief and thoughts to enable you to step out confidently in the world in a body you love.

If you scored between 56 and 100

You are right on the brink of huge changes in your life. It's as if you are standing at a crossroads and trying to decide the right direction to take. Trust that any path is the right one. There is a part of you that believes you are worth working for, even if you may not feel especially confident about yourself right now. You may have found that lack of body confidence has stopped you from doing things you would have really loved to do and that you have pushed your dreams aside or put your life on hold. You may have felt very depressed or down in the past and have tried countless ways in which to feel better, and it is this searching that will propel you forward. Underneath the lack of confidence is a belief – a desire to feel great about being you. Your soul calls for you to not give up. Believe in you! You know you are worth loving and caring about. You already have insights into how you want to feel and be, and you just need that extra something that will take you into a new world of body love, respect and confidence. Perhaps picking up this book is the next piece of the jigsaw in piecing together your own body journey.

If you scored between 101 and 155

This score indicates that you are confident in certain areas of your life and outwardly may appear to be a fairly self-assured person. You may have already done a good amount of personal/self-development work and have gained an inner strength over the years. Although you are on your way to experiencing a sense of body confidence, perhaps you have tried solving your body issues on an external level and still feel there is something missing.

You need to listen to your inner voice and follow your heart in all that you do. Try not to allow yourself to be pulled away from your own personal goals by other people, situations or events. You already know what is right for you – you now need the confidence, trust and belief to follow this through. Perhaps this book will help you to listen and take notice of the fabulous person you are. Ask yourself what you need. Look within you to find the answers you already know.

If you scored between 156 and 200

Scoring within this range indicates that you have a positive view of yourself, but there are still things that you would like to work on to achieve your ultimate sense of well-being. You may have already done a lot of soul searching and personal/self-development work but how much of what you know or have learned about yourself do you put into practice? There is a need for completion and finishing any business you have left open or pending. Follow your intuition and awareness at all times and always check back with yourself throughout your day to see how you are. **You** are your greatest strength and you also have the power to help other people achieve theirs. You know inherently what is right for you; however, there are still dreams that you would like to bring into being and it is this inner vision that you now need to follow.

At times you may be so busy 'doing' that you forget about 'being'. Put the BE back in your life – BElieve, BE loved, BE YOU!

Really 'walk your talk' and put into positive action all that you know and believe to be true for you. Forge ahead with your ideas, communicate your dreams, satisfy your needs and shine your light out into the world.

Individual Scores

Each of the different sections of the quiz gives you an awareness of where your sense of confidence may be stronger or weaker. A friend did this quiz recently and found that she scored pretty much the same on all the different sections except Influences, where her score was very much lower than the others. She realized that, whilst she might feel fairly confident in the other areas of her life, her weakest and most vulnerable area was how she was influenced by those around her. This gave her the insight to really become aware of how much of her confidence was sapped by other people's opinions and how much she adapted herself to suit the company she was in. Look at the gaps between the scores of each section. Generally, if there is a difference of more than 7, it highlights where you may need to focus your greatest attention and awareness. It also shows you where you may be experiencing the most conflict and where your actions, beliefs and feelings do not work together.

For example, scoring high in the Body/Self-Beliefs section but low in the Body Care section suggests that whilst you may have a positive attitude towards yourself and believe in your own ability, this is not passed on to your body. Your body may have become neglected. Whenever this occurs there is a sense of being at odds with yourself. How does your body know you love it if you don't show it? As with any miscommunication, a deep sense of distrust can occur as different parts of you struggle to be heard and speak the same language.

Knowing where your weaker areas are means that you can go straight to the point of conflict and begin to heal the rift from the inside out. When what you do is backed up by what you believe and how you feel is generated by who you are, then body conflict ceases to exist and you put yourself in a win–win position.

Once you know that you are stronger working **with** your body than **against** it, you will begin to harness your own inner power to create a body that you love, care about and feel totally confident in!

2.
Body Image

How much hatred have you directed at your butt and thighs
over a lifetime?
Every spring and summer there is more butt and thigh hatred
in the world than could be imagined.
  Susan Powter, *Stop the Insanity*

The Body in Your Mind

A friend showed me an old photograph of myself recently. I was on
holiday in Spain dressed in tight black leggings and a silvery glittery
swimsuit. I was wearing high heels and my hair was loose and free.
I was posing for the picture in the middle of a quiet country
road leading towards the mountains and I looked amazing! I was
shocked. I looked really good – alive, trim, sensual and confident –
someone who was at perfect ease with herself and her body.

I was shocked because I remember the day that photograph was
taken and I had felt the exact opposite. I was worried about my size
and weight. I thought I was too fat to have my picture taken. I was
worried that someone would pass by and laugh at me posing. I
recall hurrying the picture along so that I could disappear back
into some kind of no man's land and feel safe.

How sad that the 'me' in the photograph thought and believed
herself to be ugly, fat and not worth bothering with. How very sad
that I had spent the majority of my life disliking and disowning my
body. Like so many women I became lost somewhere between the
glossy magazines and the relentless diet sheets.

Looking back, I feel that I lost something more along the way –
a dream, a purity of belief in myself and who I was. I asked my

friend, 'Why didn't you tell me that I was okay – that I looked all right?' She replied that she did but I never heard her or anyone else. I shut out the loving words, the gentle praise and chose instead to hear my own punishing criticisms.

Body Illusions Create Body Panic

This is where the power of body illusion really takes hold. We stop hearing the good things that people say to us. When we look in the mirror our vision is distorted as we see a lifetime of criticisms reflected back at us. Years of being told that we were not pretty enough, clever enough or good enough blurs what we see and we begin to see what we hate. Our image becomes tainted with comparisons made to an older prettier sister, friend or acquaintance and we become sufferers of an insidious 'dis-ease' called body panic. It's a subtle disease, which affects, by and large, women who are between the ages of adolescence and death! The really crazy thing about body panic – about feeling bad about our bodies or appearance or not good enough in some way – is that it is just an illusion. It's not real.

The mental picture you have of your body is called your body image and that image is only partly shaped by the actual body you inhabit today. It's just as likely to be influenced by the body you wore when you were a child. Body memories play on inside our heads long after we have outgrown the plump, spotty, too tall or too short bodies of our childhood. Unkind or unthinking words from your parents, friends or family members may still be replaying in your mind as if they were still valid today. So many of us continue to hold on to that outdated body image. We refuse to see ourselves as we actually are. Somewhere within me, I knew that the sad, chubby child who sat alone on the garden swing kicking her legs despondently was still there – waiting to be loved and yearning to be healed. That hurt child shaped my own body image so dramatically that it was years before I could let her go and see myself in a different way.

Body Truth

Maria came to see me a year ago and as we chatted she realized that she had never known the truth about her body. She had always thought that she was fat and not very attractive. She brought in some old photo albums and showed me photographs of herself at her first ballet school dance performance, wearing her first pair of trendy jeans and acting in her school play. Every photograph brought back special memories of the diet she had been on at the time. She told me, 'I remember myself at sixteen, nearly fainting at the school disco because I hadn't eaten for three days!' She went on, the memories flooding back, 'I remember ruining my honeymoon by refusing to eat out in restaurants because I was so self-conscious and wanted my husband to think I looked fantastic and sexy in a bikini.'

The truth about her body was plain to see. Maria had suffered for over thirty years with body distrust and dislike but the truth about her body was in every photo we looked at. **She had never been fat!** This realization was a turning point for Maria. As she looked back over the photos she exclaimed, 'I can't believe I ever thought I was so fat. I mean, I wasn't thin and probably never will be but I can see I wasn't the ugly fat pig I thought I was. In fact, in most of the photos I looked really good – healthy, energetic and alive! If only I'd known it. I could have really enjoyed it.'

Those last words of Maria's really stuck in my mind – '**If only I'd known it – I could have really enjoyed it.**'

Mirror, Mirror on the Wall – Tell Me, Why Can't I See Me at All?

What do you see when you look in the mirror? Do you see an accurate representation of what you look like or does looking in the mirror provoke negative feelings and increased body dissatisfaction? Most of us don't see ourselves as others see us – most of us don't see ourselves as we are. We have become poor judges of our own appearance.

One of the reasons for this is that body image is transitory. It changes as the body changes, with age, illness, hunger, fatigue, a remark made by an unthinking colleague, or by comparing yourself to an image in a magazine or on television. A recent psychological survey found that just three minutes spent looking at pictures of models in glossy fashion magazines caused 70 per cent of women to feel depressed, guilty and shameful.

The wicked queen in the fairytale Snow White clearly suffered from a negative or distorted body image when she asked the mirror, 'Mirror, mirror on the wall, who is the fairest of them all?' The answer she received changed as she became more aware of the presence of Snow White and began to compare herself to her. For years she had been secure in her own sense of beauty and self but, as soon as she began to compare herself, she felt threatened and suddenly her body image did not match up with what she saw in the mirror. Her body had not changed, her beauty had not faded – she was the same person physically as she was the day before and yet, with the thought of Snow White uppermost in her mind, she perceived herself to be ugly, not good enough – in some way lacking. And as the story goes she then set out to destroy her rival in order that she could again reign supreme! We do the same today only nowadays we seek to hurt ourselves rather than the source of our frustration. Had the wicked queen asked herself why she felt threatened or said, 'She has her good points – I have mine,' the story might have ended with the two becoming best of friends and setting up a support network for all women who have ever felt unhappy with the way they look! It's interesting that a story told to so many of us in childhood gives the message that we have to be the most beautiful and that we must go to any lengths to achieve this.

A Day in the Life of Body Image

Body image changes from day to day, minute to minute according to how we are feeling, what we are doing, who we are with, what we hear, see or believe. Our emotions may colour our body image – for instance a friend of mine always says that she feels ugly when she is in a rage. Another friend says he feels insignificant and small whenever he perceives himself to have failed at a certain task.

We may swell with pride when we are successful or hide in shame when our actions have been less than we wanted them to be. Crying may make us feel free as we release tension and sorrow, and laughter may make us feel 'giddy' and playful as we reconnect to our childhoods.

Imagine this scenario: The morning sees you up and around at the start of your day. The sun is shining and you feel good. You walk outside and the smell of apple blossom in the air reminds you of carefree childhood holidays. You feel good about you and smile at the people you meet, nodding a happy 'hello'. Your body and self-image are high.

You get to your place of work and realize that you made an error yesterday on an important project – you feel stupid and anxious that you have let people down. Your body and self-image go down – you feel shaky, your shoulders become round and your head hangs down.

At lunchtime, you meet up with an old friend who you haven't seen for a while. She compliments you on how great you are looking. You smile and feel a little better. Your body and self-image have increased, and you find yourself sitting taller.

As you walk back into work, you notice the new receptionist laughing and chatting to your work colleagues. You wonder why you can't find it that easy to relate to people. Your body/self-image goes down a fraction as you compare yourself with her and feel let down by who you are.

On the way home you flick through the pages of a glossy women's magazine, sighing as you glance at the high fashion photographs of 'perfect' models with their 'perfect' lives. Suddenly your skirt feels way too tight and you become aware of your hips touching the person sitting next to you. Your body/self-image goes right down and you feel low and unattractive.

Later that evening a friend rings and asks if you want to go out for a drink. Still feeling low you decline and spend the evening wrapped up in a blanket of body/self-despair. As the evening goes on you might eat too much, drink too much, have an argument or just neglect yourself completely.

Your body has not changed from the morning but your body/self-image has been through a rollercoaster ride of emotions triggered by feelings, thoughts and events in your life.

What then happens (especially with women) is that instead of dealing with the events of the day in a rational way we begin to blame ourselves for not being perfect. This often then manifests itself in our relationship with our bodies and instead of talking about the issues that really matter we take a detour to our hips. We internalize feelings that we find hard to deal with and once again our bodies get the blame for our lives not being as we wish. When this happens on a daily basis we may become stuck in the world of body hate.

Body image plays a major role in how we see ourselves and the inability to feel at home in our bodies can make life miserable on every front. We are so busy obsessing over what is wrong with us – whether it's our hair, wrinkles, weight, height or features – that we fail to develop our potential as human beings. Imagine what you could achieve if you harnessed a tiny fraction of the energy and attention wasted in body hate and used it as fuel for creativity and self-development.

A Cry for Love

When we worry about our bodies we worry about who we are. When we criticize the way we look, bemoaning our large hips or crooked teeth, we are calling out to those around us to love us and accept us – to reassure us that we are really okay and that they love us the way we are. Then, perhaps if they love us we can love ourselves.

'Jackie', an ex model and client, told me that having larger breasts was what she had wanted since she was in her early teens. On her eighteenth birthday her parents surprised her by paying for surgery to enlarge her breasts. She was delighted with the results and told me how her confidence increased almost overnight. 'I loved the newfound attention my boobs gave me,' she said, 'and I felt really special and loved – my modelling work increased and I got so much more attention from men.'

All was well in her life until several years later she had to have the implants removed because of an infection. It was at this time that she experienced a total loss in her own sense of body security. Almost at once she perceived herself to be less attractive, less desirable and less loved. She described it to me as if her world suddenly fell apart. Although she still looked amazing she **felt** ugly. As we worked together she realized that her entire body image was based on her breasts. She didn't see her beautiful face or shining eyes or the graceful way she moved. She fully believed that the way people related to her was because she had great boobs. Without them, who was she? What did she have? Why would anyone want to speak to her, let alone love her? The problem is that when you only see certain parts of yourself as 'okay', you begin to deny the other parts that you feel are unacceptable. These may then become 'forgotten' or not valued or cared about. Valuing yourself and feeling good about yourself is the real secret of feeling confident in your body and developing a positive body/self-image. If you don't value something, you don't take care of it. If you don't take care of it, it becomes neglected.

Jackie's success and happiness came when she moved beyond her breasts and into her body. From an early age she equated bigger breasts with attractiveness, sexuality, attention from both men and women and love. She thought that her parents must have endorsed this also, as they paid for her operation. Outwardly, her breasts shouted to the world – look at me! Notice me! Love me! But inside she was crying out the same message to herself – look at me, notice me, love *me*!

Feeling Good About you is not a Luxury – It's an Absolute Necessity!

A lady once asked me in a workshop, 'What's wrong with changing your body by dieting, or exercising, or even by plastic surgery if it's going to make you feel better about yourself?'

The answer lies in this question: '**Is it going to make you feel better about yourself?**'

There is no certainty that losing weight will make you feel better about the person you are if you don't like or value that person to begin with. A face that is surgically 'lifted' doesn't necessarily mean that your spirits will be lifted too. Any movement towards self-improvement must be propelled not by disgust and self-rejection but by an honest acceptance of who we already are. We have been taught how to use criticism as a motivator. If you hate yourself enough, you may just motivate yourself to go to the gym more often or refuse that last slice of pizza. Self-loathing works to a degree and if you constantly see yourself as a fat ugly pig, you may manage to actually stick to a diet for a couple of weeks! Reminding yourself that your upper arms are flabby and vile may push you to do another set of triceps dips or pick up your free weights more often. For so long, body dislike has been equated with what we think is positive behaviour. However, this is positive behaviour at the expense of negative thinking!

If what you do to improve your body comes as a direct result of negative thinking, you will ruin your body image. You can work hard to have a fantastic body – but if all you ever allow yourself to see is the cellulite, what's the point?

In Tahiti I'm Beautiful!

Linda, a client, made me laugh the other day when she informed me that in Tahiti her looks and body type were highly valued and much sought after. She had been reading a magazine article featuring beauty from around the world. She explained to me, 'In Tahiti there is no such word as "diet". Tahitian women are adored for their curves.' She went on, 'Perhaps I'll go and live in Tahiti!'

Joking aside, her comments brought up the very real issue that beauty is not some hard and fast law, which has been written in stone, but an ever-changing moveable ideal, which changes from culture to culture.

For instance, in Sierra Leone, a woman's neck isn't attractive unless it's thick and fat. A tribe in Nigeria value chipped teeth and skin that is covered in scars. In Kenya long ears are sexy and the Surma women of Ethiopia desire big lips. The bigger they are, the greater a woman's price in marriage. The Knoff tribeswomen in Nigeria desire breasts to be droopy and not perky! We live in a culture that places a very high premium on physical appearance and in a time when media images are powerful forces in shaping our thoughts, values, ideals and aspirations. This all has a huge effect on our sense of self and our body image.

The Truth is not 'Out There' – It's Within Us

The truth is that there is no ideal shape and never will be. The 'perfect body' as seen in magazines and fashion shows is as transitory as a passing rain shower. Remember, you don't have to look like a supermodel to feel beautiful and sexy. Models represent the way they look – not the way we are. Next year there will be another 'look'. Big breasts are in! Freckles are out! Hair must be short and cropped! Hair must be long, shiny and straight! The Marilyn Monroe look is back! You've got to be thin to be in!

If you tried to keep up with all of the above then you would either spend all of your time having plastic surgery or you would end up by going slowly and steadily round the twist!

Unfortunately, this is exactly what many people do! When they feel insecure in their bodies many people look for an external ideal to follow. Once they have achieved that particular look or image, their own sense of body security is restored and they feel safe . . . for a time at least or until the next ideal shape or look is marketed.

How Advertising Shapes You

A friend of mine is so affected by advertising he only wears Armani suits, designer watches and Calvin Klein underwear, and drives a top-of-the-range BMW. Nothing wrong with this at all if that's what you want and you can afford it. The problem comes in that he refuses to wear anything that is not Armani and would not be seen dead in a Skoda! He lives a designer life in a designer house, eats in designer restaurants, and raises designer children. The only problem is that his wife, Marie, is **not** designer. She asked him once to go for a day wearing clothes bought from high street stores, eating food at the local takeaway and driving her car (which is not a BMW). He adores her so attempted the challenge. Within an hour he had broken it as he said he could just not go out without his Armani jacket. 'What would people think?'

On chatting to him about this he said, 'I feel a fake if I don't have my designer goods around me. I guess I've never had much of my own sense of identity so wearing Armani and driving my BMW make me feel special.' He recognizes how his own low body/self-image have led him to create a perfect image that he can buy into.

Advertising companies know this only too well and many employ top psychologists to analyze the needs, desires and issues that concern us. The biggest of these is body image and appearance. Until recently many advertisements brought you down in order to build you up with the product they were advertising. You know the type of adverts – they ask questions such as, 'Are you tense, tired, overweight, ridden with pimples? Do you have limp, lifeless hair or a limp, lifeless life? Does your skin sag? Are your eyes puffy? Do your boobs droop?'

By the end of the advert you are so depressed you are nearly screaming yes to all of the above and that's where they come dashing to your rescue – like a white knight on his charger! You are swept off your feet as you rush to buy the 'magical' product, which will save you from certain banishment from the kingdom of the beautiful!

However, times are changing and many companies are now realizing that negative advertising also has a knock-on negative effect on the consumer. By telling someone for long enough that they are not okay unless they use your product they make the person begin to feel worthless. When someone feels worth **less** they stop bothering about themselves and even your product fails to tempt them. One leading skin care and cosmetics company was clever enough to recognize the power of positive advertising and how well people respond to being told something good about themselves. Their slogan is, 'Because you're worth it!' It's clever and it promotes a feel-good factor, as on a deeper level you feel special every time you buy their product. This in turn makes you feel good, as somewhere inside you **believe** yourself to be worth it!

It is time to learn to trust ourselves, rather than the next hyped-up advertising campaign. By all means look at what is around and then take what you want from it, asking yourself the question, 'Is this me? Am I happy with this? Does this sit well with the image I have of myself?' In trusting yourself you can laugh when you read in the glossy magazines, 'Big lips are more kissable!' You know the truth – your lips are more kissable just as they are because you are at ease with your body and your life.

Free Your Mind – Love Your Body

One of the first steps towards living in a confident and happy body is to understand what having a poor body image really means to you. How does it affect you on a day-to-day level? How do you respond to compliments? Do you smile and say 'thank you' or do you shove the compliment back with an off the cuff remark like, 'You must need your eyes tested if you think that I look good!' Or do you just say nothing at all and feel acutely embarrassed?

Are there things that you won't do or places you won't go because you lack confidence in your body? Perhaps you want to change your job, take up a new hobby, start a new relationship, but you won't until you've lost weight, toned up or had a face lift!

Feeling good about you and freeing your mind from a negative body/self-image means that you live your life fully. You say 'yes' to new opportunities and 'no' when you know that something would be wrong for you.

One of my clients, Gill, is a lovely, bubbly, funny and bright person – you automatically feel drawn towards her as her beaming smile welcomes you in. The problem is that Gill welcomes in everything and everyone, which leaves her with nothing!

She complained that she always said yes to anything that came along. 'I open my mouth and there it is, "Yes" . . . before I've even thought about what it is I'm being asked. I say yes to anything and everything and then I grumble because I've got no time for me or I have to go and do all the things I've said yes to and don't want to do! The worst thing is that everyone now expects me to say yes. They say, "Oh, go and ask Gill, she'll do that for you," or "Gill won't mind." But I do mind and I'm fed up with being walked over!'

As we continued our sessions it became clear that one of the reasons that Gill always said yes was because she wanted to please people. In pleasing people she thought that they would like her more and if they liked her then perhaps they wouldn't notice the things about her that she hated.

'I guess I always feel so grateful that anyone ever includes me in anything or asks me to do things for them – I mean I'm not the greatest beauty in the world and it's just so nice to be noticed and needed!' She went on, 'I know it's awful to say this, but I even married my husband because I felt grateful to him. I couldn't imagine anyone else wanting me so I said yes (oh God, there's that word again!). Don't get me wrong, I do love him but I'm very thankful to him too!'

Gill sells herself short and her poor body image means that her life revolves around others. It's fine to do the odd thing for people if you can fit it into your schedule or if **you really want to** but, when it means that you give someone a lift home and it's three miles out of your way, or you go to watch a film you've seen twice before and didn't enjoy the first time, you have to ask yourself what's going on. Gill lives her life for other people's enjoyment – not her own. Her life is literally shaped by the image she has of herself.

If your life consists of the things that you really love to do then there are no major problems in the way you live your life. However, Gill was feeling intense conflict between her actions and her inner feelings, which was making her life intolerable.

Her own feelings of body (self) insecurity were counteracted by becoming everyone's best friend but in doing so she left out the most important person in her life: herself.

Stop Apologizing for Your Body – Applaud it!

One of the ways that Gill began to step into feeling more confident was to put a delay system in place. She had said that she would find it too hard to just say no to the things she didn't want to do so I suggested she delay her answer. Instead of responding immediately with a 'yes' she now says, 'let me have a think about it,' or, 'I'll check what I'm doing and let you know – but thanks for asking me.'

Gill reports back that this is working for her. It buys her some time and stops the automatic 'yes' answer. It also gives the message to her friends and family that Gill might have something else she wants to do and they have to begin to consider her feelings more. Gill has begun to see herself in a new light and she likes the person she is becoming. 'I feel that I do have value – no matter what I may think I look like, it doesn't matter, I count too! I feel that I am no longer apologizing for my life and body but applauding it!' Body confidence means that you begin to connect more and more to what you need at any given time. You no longer put yourself last on the list – you put yourself first. This isn't some selfish way of acting: it's vital to how you interact with your family, friends, work colleagues and the entirety of your life. When your needs are met you can help someone else to achieve theirs.

Why Wait to Live?

Putting your life on hold can mean that you are always waiting to live! Somewhere in the future you dream that your life and body will be perfect but in the meantime what happens today? The most important moment you have is right now and if it is spent worrying about how you look or actively disliking a part of yourself then you are cheating yourself on living fully. Not liking yourself today means that you will dislike yourself tomorrow and all the following days until, suddenly, you wake up aged 96 and reflect back on your life feeling sad that you never fully appreciated you or your life! Think how sad it would be to live your life for 'tomorrow' and then die before you ever reach it!

The Turning Point

Turning your thoughts around and learning to like yourself (even if it's only a tiny part of yourself) means that tomorrow will be different. Tomorrow moves you closer towards living in a happy, cherished body and experiencing the freedom that this brings.

Every time you put yourself down or feel a failure because of your appearance you are putting yourself in the role of a victim. This leaves you open to hurt and false promises. Every new diet sheet that beckons has power over you if you fail on it. Every new exercise regime lures you into its sweaty paws (even if it's totally unsuitable for your body or you hate every minute of it). You believe every unkind or personal comment made about you because on some deep level you believe them to be true. It's a no-win situation and leaves you totally powerless.

As long as your mind stays locked in battle against your body you are destined for a life-long battle between you and you. The only way to win and to go on winning is to free your mind from its caged beliefs and to choose a new way of thinking, seeing and being. You can do this right now . . .

Say to Yourself, 'I'm Okay'

No big deal – just, 'I'm okay'. You don't even have to believe it – just say it and then say it as many times as you can. Say it when you feel down, say it first thing in the morning and last thing at night, say it when you feel tempted to criticize yourself, say it to the dog, cat or budgerigar, say it when all around you is in chaos – just say it. Words are powerful and you have just given your mind a new instruction: the instruction to seek out and bring to you 'okay' feelings, thoughts and things. 'Okay' is a good place to start. It is do-able. A lady in one of my workshops once commented that she could not bring herself to say that she loved herself. It was too much, too big, the words got stuck in her throat and she felt overwhelmed. I asked her if she could say that she was okay, to which she replied that she thought she could. So, okay was where we started. She still has problems saying that she loves herself but she told me the other day on the phone that she was **very okay** and very happy!

Beliefs Have Power

The important thing to remember is that whether you say that you can do something or that you can't, you are right! If you think you are ugly or beautiful, stupid or intelligent, too fat or slim, you are right. In essence we are a collection of messages we send ourselves, which become a set of self-fulfilling prophecies. What we believe in at the present moment becomes the basis for what we believe in the next, and so on.

Beliefs are thoughts that you have about yourself which may or may not be true. Remember Maria? She believed she was fat – it wasn't true. My sister believes that she has no talent as an artist – it's not true, she draws like a dream! One of my best friends fears she cannot sing – again not true, she has a uniquely beautiful voice and a sound that is full of soul and longing. It is our beliefs that hold us back, that stop us from living our lives to the fullest. The joyful, exciting lives that we only dare to dream about become buried under deserts of self-doubt, self-dislike and self-neglect.

One of my clients was a woman in her early thirties, who had undergone surgery to reshape her nose. She had always hated it and blamed her lack of friends, relationships and success at work on it. She called it 'repulsive and disgusting'. In truth it was actually neither but the answer, to her, was to undergo plastic surgery and have it reshaped into a finer, smaller nose. She thought her life would then be better . . . more friends, a new relationship, perhaps even a promotion!

After the bruising had gone down a little the surgeon revealed her new nose to her. He was delighted with the result and awaited his client's enthusiastic response. She couldn't see the difference. She was deeply disappointed and said that she felt no different. Her nose was exactly the same and she demanded to know what he had done. He showed her the pictures taken of her nose before the operation and then asked her to look in the mirror at her new nose, which was clearly smaller and more refined. She still saw no difference. Two months later, when there was no bruising left, she still saw no difference and was furious that she had been 'taken for a ride'.

This was quite a severe example of a particular belief leading to negative body image. This woman was so used to perceiving herself as ugly and blaming all her issues on just one part of her body that she no longer saw herself as she was. Her reality had become distorted as her mind constantly reinforced her negative beliefs. Even when her appearance had changed she was so overwhelmed by her negative thoughts and feelings that she could not see herself in any other way than how she had thought she'd looked all her life. A new look and untold amounts of surgery could never reshape her own beliefs about her body.

But the exciting news is that beliefs can be changed. When you believe something to be true it literally is true. Thus, if you believe that you have a healthy, strong, beautiful body, an intelligent and enquiring mind and a passion for life itself, you automatically put yourself into the best possible state for this to happen.

Does it seem too simple? **It is simple!** Loving your body is literally only a thought away. We make life so complicated and believe that the only way we will achieve body/self-fulfilment is through hating ourselves into shape, following punishing exercise regimes or having pieces of us removed, lifted or tucked surgically. If you've tried hating your body into submission and it's left you tired, worn out and feeling worse than before – try loving it and see the difference that makes.

I Can See Clearly Now . . .

One of the ways in which you can soothe, soften and persuade your conscious mind to let go of the suffocating grip of negative body image is to work with your subconscious mind. The subconscious mind is the part of us that deals with images, visualizations, symbols and dream states. It cannot tell the difference between fantasy and reality.

Try imagining this: In front of you is the biggest, juiciest lemon you have ever seen. You pick it up and smell the tangy zest of its waxen skin. Taking a kitchen knife you slice the lemon in half and juice spurts up making you wince slightly as droplets land in your eyes. You bring the lemon closer to your lips, smelling the bittersweet aroma, and begin to open your mouth. Taking a huge bite of the lemon, your taste buds are electrified as the acidic taste smarts on your tongue. As your mouth starts to water you bite deeper into the soft citrus flesh, feeling your nose and eyes tingle from the tart tanginess.

Most people, having imagined this, will begin to feel their mouths water as saliva is produced in response to the visual image. Although you were not really eating a lemon, your subconscious mind thought that you were and immediately went into action – giving you a physical response to an imagined thought.

Sports psychologists have used the power of the subconscious mind for years to give their clients a winning edge over their competitors. Top golfers and champion tennis players harness this subconscious power by visualizing or imagining exactly where they want the ball to land. They literally see themselves playing the perfect shots again and again as they hone their skills within their subconscious minds. As they do this, their muscles are also responding by contracting and twitching as if they were playing a real game.

When you think of yourself in positive terms and see your body as something you love and are proud of then you are calling upon your subconscious mind to put you in the best possible state for this to be true. Part Two of this book, 'The Body Journey', is an entire body love and confidence quest, which harnesses the power of your subconscious mind through the process of an imaginary or visual story. How you see or perceive yourself to be is one of the most powerful keys to creating total body confidence.

Body Magic

Body magic happens when you begin to care about yourself in a loving, non-judgemental way. When you love or care about someone, you begin to nurture and treat that person on a different level. You want the best for that person and you listen to their dreams and respect their wishes.

When this person is **you**, the transformation begins and you start to feel confidence in you, your body and your life. When you care about yourself in a kind, loving way, you automatically begin to act from a higher level. You nurture yourself; you listen to your dreams, wants and wishes. You pick yourself up when you feel down and praise yourself for just being you. You no longer want to hurt yourself by unrealistic regimes forced upon your body. You begin to 'listen' to what your body really needs and become more in tune with your body's own remarkable wisdom.

With a little work, you can learn to love your body – flaws and all. Forget about a flat stomach in a fortnight – spend the next fourteen days developing a kinder view of the stomach you already have.

The Power to Change

I had thought that I was fat for so long that my mind couldn't even see me as slim when I had lost six and a half stones in weight.

I remember standing in front of a full-length mirror at a health farm as a small size 12. I was slimmer and more toned than I had ever been in my life. For the first time I could see my collarbones and the shape of my ribs. My hips and thighs were brown, long and sleek and my tummy was flatter than I had ever known it to be. This should have been the most fantastic moment in my entire life, as I had achieved everything that I had always wanted. This was the day I became 'perfect', the day the rest of my life became 'perfect'. I almost expected to hear a choir of heavenly angels around my head singing 'Hallelujah'! So why did I feel so sad?

As I looked at my new slim body, instead of the hallelujah chorus I heard an old familiar voice whispering its tight judgemental little words in my mind, 'You could still do with a few more inches off your thighs.'

My body had changed dramatically but my mind was still the same as it had always been – full of those negative thoughts and self-limiting beliefs. It was at this time that I realized I would never be happy with me, no matter how slim or toned I became. How could I ever be happy in a body which was dominated by a dissatisfied and critical mind? This was the key moment in my life when I thought enough is enough. I knew that I couldn't lose any more weight and, what's more, I really didn't want to. I was tired, fed up and depressed that all my efforts still didn't make me feel good about me. On my way home I treated myself to a cheese, tomato and pickle sandwich and for the first time in years I actually enjoyed what I was eating!

I was aware of a sense of freedom as I decided that I had tried starving me, hating me, ignoring me, punishing me, denying me and disowning me and that now I was going to try to love and accept me.

In this moment I took my first step into transforming my own body image and began my own Body Confidence Journey. It's a journey that I'm still making and every day meets me with a choice: To feel good about my life and me, or once again become the victim of body panic. I choose to feel good. And if I can do it, so can you!

> Your heart beats around one hundred thousand
> times a day.
> Your eyes take in more information than the largest
> telescope known to man.
> Your lungs inhale over two million litres of air every
> year.
> Your hearing is so sensitive it can distinguish
> between hundreds of thousands of different
> sounds.
> Your brain is more complex than the most powerful
> computer.
> You're Amazing!*

* With kind permission of BUPA

3.

Body Talk

Every time we say a negative word, we lay the mental plan for negative things. There is no escaping this law of the mind. As we think so shall it be.

Marianne Williamson, *A Return to Love*

Hey Presto!

There was once a baby elephant. Let's call him Presto. Now, Presto had grand ideas for living his life and enjoying himself but unfortunately his trainers thought otherwise. One of their training methods involved chaining baby elephants to stakes driven deep into the ground. Pull as poor Presto might he just couldn't budge the chains and remained firmly tethered to the spot. Gradually, over time, Presto became discouraged and gave up pulling. He learnt to stay put; he guessed that this was the way it was and was always going to be. The trainers were delighted and began to use lighter and lighter restraints until eventually only a small rope, attached to a stick barely anchored in the ground, stopped the now full-grown Presto from moving.

After years of conditioning Presto gave up trying to step out of his constraints and saw his life from one angle only. If only he'd been able to realize that the chains that had once held him down were no longer there and that he could be free to go anywhere he chose.

I was like that elephant – all the negative views I had of myself from childhood had bound me as tightly as poor Presto had been chained. And even when I was well into adulthood those same old chains bound and tied me to worn-out beliefs that no longer served any purpose other than to keep me exactly where I was . . .

immovable, stuck with nowhere to go. And 'Hey presto' – I became that poor elephant!

Every experience we have had from our birth has shaped our body image. From the way our parents related to us as baby and child to the influence our role models had on the way we saw ourselves. Genetically, we inherit the colour of our eyes and other physical aspects of our make-up from our parents, but mentally we begin life rather like an empty computer. As we grow up, every piece of positive or negative feedback is fed into the memory cells of that computer. This then has an impact on how we view ourselves and gradually creates the inner image on which we base all our actions and behaviour. Other people's voices become our voices until we have created our own body/self-talk, which may or may not be positive.

If the messages we have been given are consistently negative or self-limiting (especially if they come from people who matter to us) then we become like poor Presto, chained and held back by messages we have been given which may or may not be true. Eventually, we give up trying to think any other way and internalize the messages into our belief systems. It's as if we are carbon copies of all our generations before us. Our ancestors are still alive in us as we perpetuate their handed-down beliefs.

A good friend of mine who is the mother of four children once expressed how worried she was that she was damaging her children by some of the things she was saying to them. For instance, she had called one of them a clumsy clot when she had broken a new toy. She was worried that the child would grow up believing herself to be clumsy and awkward.

However, it is not necessarily the one-off comments which sink deep into our subconscious, it is the consistent message that perhaps we are not good enough which potentially alters our perception of ourselves.

As they grow older many people no longer question the beliefs they have about themselves and their lives, or whether their opinions are truly theirs and not their parents'. A friend of mine says that she always votes Conservative. Out of curiosity one day I asked her why. She replied that she didn't really know but that her parents always voted Conservative so she did too.

Another friend of mine remembers her mother telling her that she would never amount to anything. Her mother felt deeply hurt that she had never been allowed to pursue her dreams of becoming an artist and viewed her daughter as 'competition', so she told her this regularly.

In my own case the negative messages were reinforced daily. Although I knew I was loved, I also felt unacceptable as I was. Relatives would comment on my weight before they had even said hello to me. At school I was tormented by the fashionable 'in crowd' who made it very clear that I would never be accepted into their lofty lair. My true friends (whom I still keep in contact with today) tried to help me through but it was hard to listen to their words of love and support over a screaming sea of insults and unkind comments! This is why our own inner voices need to be heard. We need to shout louder, proclaiming that we are fabulous individuals. We need to counteract the years of talking ourselves down by talking ourselves up. For every negative or unhelpful thought you have to put two positive ones in its place.

Nice Face – Shame About the Body!

I remember a complete stranger coming up to my mother when we were on holiday one year and pointing at me as she said, 'She has such a pretty face, what a pity she's so fat!' Over the next few years I remember being aware that any time a similar comment was made, I began to only see my face and felt rather like the disembodied grinning Cheshire cat in *Alice in Wonderland*. The rest of my body began to disappear under shapeless fabrics where I could try to forget that it really existed. In this way my own particular body story began to manifest itself as I began to think, feel and speak of my body in negative ways. Thus, the image I was to have of myself was already being shaped and the layers of negativity I carried would take years to undo.

Beached Whale in a Raincoat!

I love this story told to me by Janet, a lady who attended one of my workshops. She explained that she absolutely loves swimming (especially in the sea), so when a friend of hers invited her to Spain on holiday she was delighted. However, her delight turned to apprehension and inner fear when she noticed just how far the beach stretched before it reached the sea. The tide seemed to make no difference to the distance and Janet felt dismayed at the thought of walking to the sea in just her swimsuit. She wondered if she should just swim in the hotel pool but it was really quite small and seemed to be full of children and beach balls!

She spent the night trying to think of ways in which she could disguise her body, which she felt was just too large to be seen without a cover-up. (Janet was a size 14!)

She discounted the thought of a towel tied around her hips or a sarong and went instead for the raincoat she had worn on the journey from London. She figured that this would cover all of her body and would be the best camouflage. She laughed loudly at the memories of herself walking down the beach on a hot summer's day in a raincoat and went on to say, 'I must have been mad to have thought that I wouldn't be noticed wearing a raincoat – talk about standing out! I felt ridiculous!'

Janet can laugh about her experience now but at the time it was very real and very painful for her. 'I was so obsessed with covering myself up that I never even thought of how wearing my raincoat would look.' She went on to say, 'The next day I went down to the sea in my sarong and although I felt hugely self-conscious I was aware that no one seemed to be giving me a second glance – everyone was just getting on with enjoying themselves and being involved in their own lives.'

Janet's story shows how the negative thoughts and images she has of her body caused her to lose touch with the reality of her body. In reality she is a size 14 with a perfectly fine figure – in her mind she resembles a whale! Everything she does in her life is done with one action plan in mind – to hide the whale she believes she is. No amount of compliments or reassurances from others has any impact on the way she chooses to view herself and subsequently live her life. What is so sad is that Janet hides herself from every part of her life; she hides from her husband (romantically and sexually), she hides from work by feeling she is inadequate (and has been passed over in favour of someone else for promotion), she hides her feelings, her dreams and ultimately who she really is. As Janet continues to work with her body image she is gradually coming out of hiding, and one of her greatest achievements was being able to take off that raincoat and walk down the beach in a sarong!

More Than the Sum of our Parts

A friend of mine, Mike, told me about his experience with an extremely attractive woman he met at a party. He told me, 'I really fancied her and she looked like just the kind of woman I would love to meet so I was delighted when I was introduced to her.' He went on, 'After chatting for about ten minutes or so I became aware of what she was saying about herself. She seemed to be taking her features apart piece by piece and holding them up for inspection.' He explained that she began talking about her face and within seconds had pointed out that her eyes were actually too far apart, her nose was crooked, her teeth were off-centre and her chin receded a little.

I was fascinated by how he responded to this and asked him how he felt as his companion continued to dissect her own face and body. He replied, 'The weird thing was that the more she went on pointing out how unattractive she was, the more unattractive she seemed to become! I mean, her eyes probably were widely spaced and her nose was a bit crooked but I didn't even notice that before. I saw her as the whole picture and not imperfect parts, which stood alone. It was sad really as her most unattractive feature was her attitude towards herself!'

Mike didn't pursue the encounter.

Does my Bum Look Baggy in This?

I remember an aerobics class I was about to teach when a new member joined the class. She was very concerned that everyone would be looking at what she called her 'baggy bum'! I assured her that she shouldn't worry, as everyone else was normally too preoccupied with thoughts of their own 'baggy bums' to even notice anyone else's! This made me think of all the wonderful things we miss or don't see in our lives because we are so caught up in our own body and self anxieties. We worry that people will see what we most despise and we usually draw this towards us by how we act, think and refer to ourselves! We are so locked away in our worlds of body imperfections that we fail to see how spectacular the world around us can be.

Who Lives in a Body Like This?

There is a television programme called *Through the Keyhole* in which celebrity guests have to guess whose house is being shown by unravelling a series of clues which are evident within the house itself. After the clues the panel is asked, 'Who lives in a house like this?' and they try to work out the answer.

Over the years that I have been counselling I have been amazed to see how we, as people, give clues about who we are and, more importantly, what we think of ourselves by the way we talk about ourselves. It's as if subtly we are trying to find out, 'Who lives in a body like this?' – who are we?

Body Clues

For the next week or so try really listening to what your friends, family, colleagues and even strangers say about themselves. Do they undermine their achievements? Are they embarrassed by praise or do they accept it openly and warmly? Do they put themselves down in conversation or do they have a realistic attitude towards themselves – expressing both their good and not-so-good attributes? Listen to the words they use – how often do they say words such as 'I ought to,' 'I should,' 'I can't,' 'I'm no good at,' 'If only I wasn't,' etc. Gently gather together the clues that people give you in everyday life so that you get a better picture of their own unique body and self-talk.

Listen to What you Say

The week after that, listen to yourself. Often it is easier to hear the clues in other people first before you begin to 'listen' to yourself. Pay great attention to the words you use. Imagine you are an interested observer in your own life – you are not there to judge, condemn or criticize – just observe with interest. The results are often quite illuminating!

Sarah, a client, was amazed by just how many times she said to her two daughters (both now in their twenties), 'Do you think you should?' She recognized this as something her mother had also said to her whenever she had suggested doing something new. One of her daughters had told her that she was thinking of opening a shop with a friend and before she could stop herself the words were out – 'Do you think you should, dear?' As we talked about her 'discovery' Sarah remembered all the times she had wanted to try a new venture, go to a new place or just buy a new dress. The comment from her mum was always the same – 'Do you think you should?' Sarah described how it made her feel that it was unsafe to try anything new, to take risks and ultimately that maybe her ideas were not very good ones!

Sarah had continued to replay her mother's belief, which was founded upon fear, anxiety and lack of trust that anything she did would be okay. She had just repeated the pattern without questioning if this was how **she** felt or if it was true for her. By becoming aware of the words she was using and the messages she was giving, Sarah could take a step closer to interrupting those patterns and change the belief to a more positive and empowering one.

'Listen' to what you say about yourself, your family, your work, your dreams, your partner, your needs, wants and desires. Become the watcher of you. Remember, the clues are there.

Listen especially to what you say about your body. Do you point out your faults? Do you compare yourself to others and feel that you lack what they have? Do you make excuses not to do things that you would really love to do because you feel insecure or unhappy about the way you look?

Listen to What you Don't Say

As well as listening to what you are saying it is also really good fun and probably even more important to 'listen' to the words and the thoughts that you don't say. These are all the times that you keep your mouth firmly closed but the thoughts are whizzing around in your head. Maybe you want to say something but for one reason or another you don't – you keep quiet. Notice the quiet moments and become aware of the feelings behind the thoughts. What is it you want to say but don't? Ask yourself if it is okay that these words are left unsaid. There is no right or wrong in this, just awareness, an observation of you. By listening to what you don't say – listening to your thoughts – you'll really begin to understand yourself better.

Change the Words and Change the Perception

A work colleague told me this great story about a friend of hers who was interviewed for a national radio station. She had written a book about fashion for the fuller figure and had been asked in to give some tips 'on air'. As a part of her introduction the radio presenter referred to her as fat, and she gently but firmly said that she objected to this, as the word 'fat' had negative associations for her. She went on to ask him to come up with at least five other adjectives to describe her. He struggled as he came up with words such as buxom, voluptuous, well-rounded, well-padded, etc. When he had finished she suggested that he tried 'beautiful' because that is how she thinks of herself.

What a fabulous example of body confidence! She not only sees herself as a beautiful woman in her own right but also affirms to others that this is the way she wishes to be perceived.

When the words you use about yourself are positive, enhancing, loving, kind and uplifting then you send out a very clear message to those around you that this is the way you wish to be seen. So, the next time you begin to criticize a part of yourself for not being 'perfect' or 'good enough', stop and listen to the words you are using. If they are negative to you then try to think of another, more positively powerful way to describe yourself.

Equally, do not let others describe you in ways that are at odds with how you wish to see yourself. A friend once commented that her family always jokingly referred to her as the 'runt of the litter' because she was small and very slim. After years of hearing this she finally became exasperated with it and told her family that she preferred to think of herself as being small and beautifully formed. She told them that it wasn't the quantity that mattered but the quality and she certainly had that. To her complete surprise they agreed with her and were totally unaware of the negative effect that their previous comments had had.

Words have power – power to conjure up images in your mind, which translate into feelings. 'Runt of the litter' produces an image of a small, rather sickly animal that is struggling to survive. By changing the words to 'small and beautifully formed' my friend created an image of herself which said that she was just right!

Change Dull, Boring, Worn-Out Words to Bright, Happy, Shiny Ones!

How do you respond when someone asks you how you are or how are you doing? Do you say that you are 'so-so' or 'not bad' or even that you 'mustn't grumble'? Very often we just reply with a bland, all-encompassing 'fine'. When I was in training to become a psychotherapist we had an interpretation for what 'fine' really meant – Freaked, Insecure, Neurotic and Emotional! This always makes me think twice before I'm about to say that I'm fine! The next time you are asked how you are, try responding with something that's going to shoot straight into your neural pathways and make your mind tingle with pleasure and excitement! Try replying that you are feeling fantastic or that things couldn't be better or that you are on top of the world! Here are some other ideas of happy, shiny words you could use:

> **I'm feeling . . .**
> ★ Energized
> ★ Outrageous
> ★ Just the best I can be
> ★ Fantastic
> ★ Really happy
> ★ Brilliant

Feng Shui for Your Mind and Body – Clear the Body Clutter!

The ancient Chinese art of Feng Shui believes that energy (or Chi) may become trapped in places where there is clutter, mess, or items which are not conducive to your sense of well-being and health. Feng Shui masters advocate evaluating what you have around your home and if it is not something you love, which serves a purpose, makes you feel great or brings you happy memories, then get rid of it.

It is the same with our thoughts – just as you clear out your rooms to allow the energy to flow more freely, you can clear your thoughts so that you too begin to move freely in a body which is at ease with itself.

Body clutter, like the clutter we allow to accumulate in our homes, may be an outward sign that we are stuck or have become clogged up, weighed down or overwhelmed in some way.

I have identified four main areas where body clutter is likely to build up. These are:

1 **Mind clutter** These are any thoughts you have which are negative, unhelpful, unkind, damaging or hurtful to your body in any way. They include ritualistic or addictive behavioural patterns, for instance, getting stuck in any form of obsessive behaviour like rigid exercising, strict adherence to a diet sheet so that feelings of guilt are formed when any 'forbidden' foods are consumed, and talking yourself down, believing that you have no value, esteem or worth.

2 **Body blocks (unfinished body clutter)** When a body is neglected in any way it becomes fragmented, causing energy blocks in different areas, which stifle the body's natural energy flow. This involves any part of your body that you have neglected and needs attention – for instance, visiting the dentist, optician, chiropodist, physiotherapist or just having a medical check up. Essentially, it is about unfinished body business and making sure that you look after and take care of any part of your body which is in need of extra love and attention. Many different complementary therapies such as

acupuncture, acupressure, homeopathy and reflexology can help restore low energy levels, and exercise such as tai chi, Pilates or yoga may be beneficial in channelling and maximizing your body's energy flow. You may think that you can ignore that nagging lower back pain you've had for a while but your subconscious mind knows that it's there and will keep reminding you of its presence until you take notice – dragging your energy and confidence down in the meantime.

3 **Body hoarding** This refers to any thing you collect but never use that has a specific body-related purpose, like fitness videos that you never actually do any more, exercise bikes or equipment that is just left gathering dust somewhere and any body lotions or gadgets which are not being used. If you haven't used any item in the last six months just re-evaluate its purpose and decide whether you will use it again. If not, get rid of it, or give it away to someone who would have a use for it. I had a foot spa for years – it was given to me as a Christmas present, but I never used it – not once. In spite of never using it I also found it extremely hard to let go of, as in the back of my mind was the thought that I **might** use it one day! Eventually I gave it to a friend who was delighted with it and loves to treat herself after a hard day. Holding on to any body gadgets that you don't use can also make you feel guilty, pressured or can lead to a case of the 'should's. You 'should' do a fitness video, you 'should' ride the bike, you 'should' use that very expensive but time-consuming leg cream and you 'should' eat that three-month supply of calorie-counted biscuits! Do what you love and love what you do and if it doesn't excite, delight, motivate, inspire or enthuse you with a sense of well-being – let it go and make room for something that does!

4 **Unwanted body clutter** This applies to those entirely negative, depressing and ultimately judgemental comments made by other people. Refuse to collect any more body clutter by not taking on board anyone else's ideas about how they perceive you. Like an unwanted gift – get rid of it. It does you no good to hold on to it and it certainly doesn't help the person who gave it to you. Refuse to collect any more negative comments by gently but firmly handing them back – thanking them for their interest but stating that you have other ideas and beliefs about who and how you are and what is best for you.

Start by resisting the urge to put yourself down in any way when engaging in conversation. You don't have to shout out that you think you're wonderful – you just need to think it!

Leave the Body Garbage Club!

It's as if we all secretly enrolled in the body garbage club, where the rules are simple – that we think unpleasant thoughts about our bodies, say unkind words about ourselves, compare ourselves to everyone else and engage in behaviour which limits or hurts us. For the club to survive its main rule must be strictly followed – that we must all feel like garbage and keep talking rubbish about ourselves! Watch out for members of the body garbage club – they can be found everywhere and in any place groups of women (in particular) get together or exchange conversation. Signs to look out for are:

1 Comparing their bodies and commenting negatively on their own.
2 Judging other women's bodies.
3 Obsessing over the latest diet/fitness fad.
4 Talking themselves down instead of up.

The worst thing about this club is that membership of it can become addictive – each time we say, think or feel negatively about our bodies we strengthen that belief. With enough repetitions and emotional intensity, we can find ourselves compelled to have these feelings or behave in this way **consistently**. Anthony Robbins sums this up perfectly in his book *Awaken the Giant Within* (page 124), 'We've got to remember that we get whatever we focus on in life. If we keep focusing on what we don't want, we'll have more of it.'

Leave the body garbage club by dumping all the unkind words, thoughts and beliefs you may have about your body and self. Put them where they belong – in the bin! They do you no good at all. All they do is weigh you down, clutter your mind, and eventually stagnate and poison you! A friend of mine commented that she found this hard to do at first as she was so used to indulging in two main topics of conversation when she was with friends – the first was men, the second was losing weight.

However, the rules of the club dictate that it's how you perceive yourself to be that makes you a valid member. She told me, 'At first it was really difficult and strange not to pull my body apart along with the others. I mean we would all laugh and joke about our bums, stomachs, breasts or whatever part of us we didn't much like. I found that I stopped talking at all as I felt I couldn't join in and it made me feel a bit left out I suppose. After a while everyone began to comment on how quiet I had become and they wondered if I was all right. I decided that I would tell them that I was trying to think of myself in a more positive way and was trying to clear my body clutter. I thought that they would all laugh at me but was shocked to see that they were all really interested in what I was doing.' I asked her what happened after that. She replied, 'The amazing thing was that we all decided to put a ban on referring to ourselves in a limiting or unkind way and made a point of discussing and sharing the dreams, values, ideas and issues which were important to us and our hopes for the future. More importantly, we all began to support each other and suddenly we were really talking and I found out things about them that I had never known before. We went deeper than our bodies and found the people underneath.'

My friend's experience was enlightening as it shows how, by constantly being bound up in our own body concerns, we perpetuate the problem. The body garbage club exists only as long as we all buy into it and fuel it with words which betray us. So, remember that the next time you refer to your legs as 'thunder thighs' you are telling others that this is how you see yourself and how you wish to be seen by them. Tell yourself gently, with love and humour, that you're talking rubbish and hand in your resignation to the body garbage mindset.

The Body Talk Quiz

The following messages (both negative and positive) were compiled from things that many of my clients and workshop participants had heard from various people in their life – parents, siblings, aunts and uncles, friends, acquaintances, school teachers, employers, even strangers.

Read through the list and just tick any that seem familiar or that you might have also heard or experienced as you grew up (adding in any other sayings or comments of your own).

Negative messages

- ★ Why can't you be more like your sister/friend/cousin, etc?
- ★ I told you so
- ★ You can do better than that
- ★ Don't talk about sex
- ★ You're not going out looking like that are you?
- ★ Anything worth doing is worth doing well
- ★ I expected more of you
- ★ You'll never amount to anything
- ★ If you just lost a bit of weight . . .
- ★ What's wrong with you?
- ★ Don't cry!
- ★ Don't say anything unless you can say something nice

★ Do you think you should?
★ You'd look better if you did your hair this way . . .
★ You're useless
★ Can't you ever get it right?
★ I'm embarrassed to be seen with you
★ You look tired
★ You'd be okay if you would just . . .
★ To be successful you've got to be thin

Positive messages

★ You are a very special person
★ I'm sorry, you are right
★ Keep up the good work
★ Sometimes tears are refreshing
★ Good for you!
★ That was a really good idea you had
★ I love you just the way you are
★ It's a pleasure to work with you
★ I find you very attractive
★ You're beautiful
★ Do what makes you happy
★ You're really good fun to be around
★ Everybody makes mistakes – you'll probably learn from it
★ As long as you enjoy what you do – that's what counts
★ Wear what you feel good in
★ I'll support you in whatever decision you make
★ You're creative and original
★ It's okay to feel angry – feelings need to be expressed
★ I love you
★ Do what **you** think is right

Now, just notice how many ticks you got for either the positive or negative statements. Did any one dominate or were your messages fairly equal, affirming both the positive and the negative?

This just gives you a clue to the amount of negative and positive 'backchat' that you may have been subjected to whilst growing up and becoming an adult. If the more negative comments heavily outweigh the positive ones then this may be reflected in how you see yourself and how deeply you feel towards your body.

Sometimes you may not remember receiving any clear body/self messages, either positive or negative. A friend of mine completed the body talk quiz and was surprised to realize that her parents had never particularly commented on what she was doing, how it should be done or what she looked like. I wondered what kind of an impact that had had on her, to which she replied, 'I suppose I began searching for my own body (self) messages – I remember watching the other children in the school playground, how they teased and played with each other and formed their own special clubs. Later in my teens I would read as much as I could on inspiring people – Madame Curie, Einstein and the stories of rock stars who had 'made it'. I guess I was looking for an identity.'

It is interesting that the lack of any overt body/self messages leads to the need to create some kind of inner/self dialogue, and in my friend's case she sought out the most inspirational people to model herself upon. I wondered if her experience had had a positive effect on her life, to which she replied, 'I'm not sure. I always felt that my parents didn't really mind too much what I did – perhaps that could be interpreted as not caring – but I think they did in their own way. I remember just feeling invisible.'

Although my friend can't recall any particular messages it is clear that she still picked up her own set of inner talk. She has a dream of making it to the top in the music profession so perhaps her feelings of being invisible as a child have led her to seek out the biggest and brightest way to become totally visible to all around. In essence, her parents, by their lack of comment, actually made the biggest statement of all – they showed their disinterest.

Our sense of self-esteem is based largely on the positive responses from others. The problem comes when others praise you because it suits their own agenda. For example, Cathy (a lady I met in one of my workshops) told the group how she had studied ballet from the age of four and how at every opportunity her mother would encourage her to dance for their family, friends and neighbours. Cathy continues the story, 'I was okay with performing at the drop of a hat when I was younger and my mum would stand back, smiling and clapping as I showed off my pirouettes, splits and arabesques. And as long as I was doing what she wanted it was fine. But as I grew older I didn't want to perform in front of the family and neighbours any more and said so. Well! That was it! My mother was furious that she could not show me off any more and told me that I was a spoilsport and too big to ever make it as a ballerina anyway!'

Cathy realized that her messages were **always** conditional on how well she was behaving or if she was doing something to please another person. She went on to tell us that later in her teens she developed anorexia nervosa and was hospitalized three times before being able to come to terms with who she really was and what she truly desired from her life. She still struggles today with the image she has of herself but has worked to create her own inner body talk which she finds supports and comforts her if she is feeling particularly stressed and tempted to stop eating again. (More on anorexia and other eating disorders in Chapter Six, Body Hurt.)

If the messages we absorb are predominantly full of fear, based on the negative and conditional, or do not empower us, then it may lead to a loss of our sense of self. When someone has very little confidence in themselves, their abilities or their power to achieve their dreams, several things may happen. One is that they begin to hide the person they are and develop an inner and outer face. Outwardly, they may show a positive or capable front to the world, whilst on an inner level they may feel insecure or uncertain of their place in this world. People with a negative inner face may tend to act out their feelings of lack, insecurity or inferiority – the salesman who believes he can't sell will create situations to support his belief. He will find it hard to sell even to a willing buyer! The student who believes he/she will fail his/her exams will more than likely bring about that result. The beautiful girl, who sees herself as ugly, may feel uncomfortable in social and romantic settings and unwittingly communicate this anxiety to any potential admirers, causing them to back off, thus fulfilling her inner concept of just how ugly she believes she is.

Body Predictions

What we say about ourselves matters – it's important. What we tell our children is vital if they are to grow up loving their bodies and themselves. I have seen children of eight years old already being pulled apart by low self-esteem and negative body image. Many are already on the downhill and dangerous path of eating distress.

These children are often the subjects of what I call 'body predictions'. This is when a parent, family member, teacher or anyone closely associated with the family predicts how a child will be. Very often, these predictions are unconscious and may come about as a result of comparing the child to an older sibling, or even a close friend.

A friend of mine remembers her mother always comparing her to a good friend of hers, saying, 'Why can't you be more like Angela?' and 'Angela would never do that!' It left her feeling resentful of her mother and also of Angela, who she came to view as the 'perfect' person. She recalls yelling at her mother in a fit of temper one day, 'Why don't you have Angela as your daughter – you certainly don't think that I'm good enough!'

Gemma used to come to my dance classes. She loved it and enjoyed expressing her feelings through dancing. One day she came into class looking as if she had been crying. I asked her what was wrong and she asked me what exercises she could do to get rid of her 'saddlebags'. I asked her why she thought that she had 'saddlebags', to which she replied, 'My mum said that she wished I was more like my twin sister Geraldine who didn't have "saddlebags". She said that I was obviously going to be the fat one.'

Another child once asked me how she could get rid of her pot belly! She told me that she did 100 sit ups every night and wasn't going to eat crisps or chocolate anymore.

Somewhere along the line she had got the message that she had a pot belly, which wasn't acceptable. When I met her mother after the annual school dance show I realized where this prediction had come from. I was congratulating the child on doing so well when her mother simply commented that she didn't know where her daughter got her talent. She remarked that it was unlikely to be her father as he had two left feet and that as her daughter took after herself it was useless even to contemplate dance as a serious career. She explained, 'You see, she takes after my side of the family and we all have pot bellies and no chests! I call us the pot-belly piglets.'

What is so sad is that both these children were under ten years old, and they were already worrying that they were not good enough. Neither one had a weight problem, let alone 'saddlebags' or a 'pot belly'.

They had picked up messages from their mothers that neither of them was okay as they were and in order to be loved or appreciated they had to change a part of themselves. What is heartbreaking is that instead of enjoying their childhood they were both embarking on a long, lonely journey of body angst. However, body predictions can come from anywhere – not just from within the family setting. Schoolteachers and the media also have a huge impact on the way children perceive themselves to be, as do pop stars and movie stars who all spread the message of what is or isn't acceptable. Thus, the teenager who isn't a Britney Spears look-alike may feel at a loss as to whom she is if she hasn't been encouraged to create her own identity and sense of self.

It is vital that we listen to the words we say about ourselves – to ourselves and to those around us – and to make sure that those words are powerfully positive and uplifting. It is vital that we learn to love ourselves, feel at home in our bodies and honour our own special talents and abilities. If we can grow from our own pain, forgive and let go of the messages that may have trapped and darkened our light, then we can pass on the most important message to our children – that they are okay exactly as they are, that they are lovable and unique and that anything is possible in this lifetime!

Kate Winslet, the beautiful, charismatic star of the film *Titanic*, remembers her own childhood, having gone through her own eating distress. She recalls: 'I was that child, looking at the images of models in films, magazines, fashion shows. This is what girls are brought up to believe, that to be thin is to be loved, adored, perfect.'

Believe in You

One of the ways to begin to increase your own sense of body confidence and free yourself from negative thoughts is to write down your own body/self-beliefs. Remember that beliefs are created from past messages, which you accumulated over time and stored in your 'computer' mind. If these messages were mainly negative and constantly reinforced by others around you then you may have turned that message into a belief.

Think back to Presto – he had been chained for so long that even when the chains were removed he was conditioned into believing that he could not move. Eventually no chains were needed – his own mind held him prisoner! Really begin to question and look at the things you say about yourself and the things others say about you. Ask yourself, 'Is this true? Is this how I feel? Is this how I am? Do I believe this?' If the answers are yes to all of the above then fine, there's no conflict. But, if you answer no, then it highlights an inner tension or conflict between you and you. There arises a discrepancy between your true self and your false self (or the self that you have adapted to fit someone else's view).

Remember Gill in Chapter Two, doing everything to please everyone else but secretly resenting and hating it. Her true self wanted to say no but her adapted self – the self that she showed to people – went on living the lie, causing great inner turmoil, conflict and unhappiness.

Change the CD

Imagine that you put on a CD but you've selected an old compilation that you actually don't like very much any more. What are you going to do? Do you sit through it anyway, cringing through the songs and putting yourself through agony? Or do you simply change the CD? It's easy – you change the CD. Essentially, that's what body talk is about – changing the CD!

If your beliefs about yourself hold you down, keep you stuck in self-dislike or body despair and do nothing to enhance your feelings of inner and outer confidence – then change them!

No one and nothing can make you feel bad about yourself – only **you** can! This is exciting, because it means that if you are the only person who can make you unhappy or feel down/unconfident, low, etc, then the reverse is also true. **You** are the only one who has the power to make you feel great, fantastic, confident and joyful in your life and body. It's up to you how you choose to think and what you choose to believe about yourself.

I could have gone on believing that I was too fat, unconfident and unattractive to do anything productive in my life, to even bother dreaming my dreams, but my true self – the part of me that believed in me – kept calling out to be heard. And eventually, when I had beaten myself down by beating myself up, I crept out of the cage in my mind, sniffed the air and thought that there has to be a better way to live!

No one has the power to hurt you – only you can do that. If someone tells you that you are stupid, unattractive, uncool or whatever, you have two options:

1 You can believe them and feel hurt and upset – your confidence shattered.
2 You can point out that this is only their opinion and that you prefer to stick with the more positive image that you have of yourself.

In Part Two, The Body Journey, you will be asked to create new beliefs about yourself, but until then, from this moment on, question the beliefs you have. Are they true for you? If they're not – change the CD, put another belief in its place.

If I still had the same beliefs that I had about myself when I was growing up and in my twenties I could imagine how the phone call to present a fitness slot on national television might have gone:

> TV PRODUCER: We'd love you to present our fitness slot – how about it?
>
> ME (then): Thanks but I'm really sorry I can't do it. (Thoughts unsaid – You see I believe I'm too fat and ugly and why would you want me anyway – *are* you nuts?)

Looking back, I remember what I actually did say:

> ME: Wow, thank you, I'd love to – how brilliant!! When do you want me?

Anthony Robbins, in his book *Unlimited Power* (page 64), has some thought-provoking ideas on the power of beliefs: 'The trick is to choose the beliefs that are conducive to success and the results you want and to discard the ones that hold you back.' He also points out on pages 64–5 that, 'When you congruently say you can, you give a command to your nervous system that opens up the pathways to the part of your brain that can potentially deliver the answers you need.'

One of my old beliefs was that I was fat and therefore disgusting. I changed it to, 'Fat is just fat – I am more than my size. I am strong, lovable and creative.'

A client, 'Suzy', changed her belief of 'I'm so ugly – I hate the way I look,' to 'This is my face and in it I see wisdom, beauty and compassion – it's a face to love.'

The Wish Becomes the Woman

A lady in a workshop once said that if she told herself she was lovely, it would be a lie. Her beliefs had an extremely strong hold on how she saw herself. She was near to tears as she asked to talk to me at the end of the day. She explained, 'You see I don't believe that I'm worth anything. I'm not lovely, clever, talented or even worth bothering with.' I asked her why she came to the workshop and she replied, 'Because I want to change – I don't want to be like this anymore!'

I gently said, 'If you are here because you want to change then you must believe you are **worth** changing. You gave up your time to be here, paid for a ticket, travelled to get here – that sounds like you think you're worth bothering with doesn't it?'

At that moment her face changed completely – the hard worry lines in her forehead softened, her jaw relaxed, her eyes shone with light and realization and for the first time – she smiled. She got it!

'I guess I must think I'm worth bothering with or you're right – I wouldn't be here!'

In a second she changed a belief of fifty years!

Body magic happens and the wish becomes the woman!

4.

Body Conscious

The future's a mystery, the past is history, and the present's a gift – that's why it's called 'the present'.

How are you? I mean how are you right now – right at this very moment? How are you feeling? How is your emotional state? Are you happy, sad, worried, excited, anxious, calm? How is your physical state? Do you feel hungry or thirsty? Are you hot or cold? Are you aware of any tiredness and if so where in your body are you feeling tired? Become aware of the shape your body is creating as you read this page. Do you need to change your position to something more comfortable? How is your breathing – fast, slow, deep or shallow? Do you find yourself holding your breath if you feel tense? Do you need to visit the toilet but are just waiting until you finish this chapter? How is your mental state? Are you reading this and really absorbing every word in the moment or do you find your mind wandering off to those chores that you have yet to do or to a work project for tomorrow? How is your mind? Where is your mind? Are you living fully in the present or escaping back to the past. Are you sneaking off into the future dreaming of being somewhere else or someone else?

Be honest – there's no one else here but you and me and only you know the answers to these questions. There's no right or wrong way to answer and there's no catch, they are just there to prompt you into becoming more aware of how you are – right here, right now.

Rent a Body!

Many people never really live in their bodies – it's as if they are renting their bodies out on a long-term lease with yearly options to buy or continue renting. Living in your body means that you own it and take full responsibility for how you treat, love, look after, nurture, comfort and pleasure you. It's about becoming aware of **who** and **how** you are at any given moment. Owning and loving your body means that you notice when you are tired, frustrated, happy or anxious and acknowledge that these feelings are your reality – they are true for you and as such, you have the power to change the state you are in. There isn't a landlord waiting in the wings for us to hand our bodies over to when something needs fixing or when we want the décor changed! Unfortunately for many people it's as if they enjoy renting while it's good but as soon as something goes wrong they throw their hands in the air with a cry of, 'Help – I didn't do anything, it's not my fault – you fix it!'

The same applies to our bodies. When we neglect or mistreat ourselves we may end up lacking energy or suffering with illness, and then we expect the doctor to fix us up straight away. But what's really needed is a more caring attitude towards ourselves. I rented my body for years – it was never really mine, not whilst I was always dreaming of a 'perfect' tomorrow when I would become automatically confident, beautiful and as thin as a pencil! I lived in tomorrow – you must have heard of it – it's that place where things are better, worries are over, your clothes hang just right, relationships are always fulfilling and the sun will always come out!

Gall Blimey – That's a Lot of Stones!

In renting my body I also ignored my body. I lost touch completely with how I was really feeling. My body didn't matter and it was really as if I was just a sitting tenant who didn't care much about the place I lived in. The paint could be peeling off the walls, the floorboards rotten and damp but I wouldn't notice. I was never aware that the electrics could do with rewiring and the whole place was just in desperate need of some love, care and attention. In my mind I rented and, to be honest, wasn't even there most of the time! I didn't **want** to be there – my body was and had been the source of so much pain, sadness and pure frustration for so much of my life – why would I want to stay there? However, all the time I spent hating my body it was quietly loving and keeping me safe. For every ugly word I ever shouted at my body and my self, my body kept on working to keep me in optimum health and well-being. Whilst I ignored me, my body began to try and warn me that something was very wrong.

I didn't listen when I awoke one night with pain in my upper back and abdomen – I put it down to eating something that hadn't agreed with me. A month later the pain was worse and I woke up sweating and in agony. I ignored it, laughed it off. Two weeks later it was back – stronger this time and determined to make me listen. I didn't! Everyone begged me to see the doctor – I refused: 'It was nothing,' I said.

Four months on and 'nothing' was really 'something' – the pain was coming in waves of nausea every night, gripping around my body with its vice-like claws until finally one night I screamed out that I couldn't take it anymore. I lay on the bathroom floor shaking with agony and feeling as if I was going to die. An ambulance was called and I was rushed to hospital in an emergency situation. They operated and removed my gall bladder plus 46 gall stones (the size of chick peas)!

By not accepting where I was and how I was feeling, by ignoring me, I put myself in danger and caused huge amounts of worry to those around me who did love and care about me.

The Body's Bittersweet Symphony

Looking back on this episode I realize that my body was not only trying to warn me of imminent danger and a serious health problem but that it was literally also trying to get rid of the bitterness I felt towards myself and others. Bile is bitter – representing perhaps the bitterness within us – within me. Over the years my resentments, frustrations, anger and bitterness hardened and I realized that I was feeling 'galled' and had developed a 'stony' attitude towards others and my self. My body, in its own unique way, was trying so hard to rid me of the bitterness I was carrying around and when I refused to listen it took over, forcing me to hear my own cry!

It's as if each one of us has our own unique, beautiful song or symphony, which is constantly being composed as we change, grow and move beyond our limitations. The more we are aware of our bodies, needs, dreams, thoughts and actions the more harmonious the song we hear. When we lose touch with who we are or ignore aspects of ourselves which need healing, love or attention the body symphony begins to change – things sound and feel a little discordant, leaving us feeling out of balance and 'out of tune' with ourselves. In my case my body lost its melody, forgot the words and became increasingly painful to listen to as it began to play only one note again and again – striking out more of a warning siren than a full symphony!

Any physical pain or tension alerts us to the fact that something is out of balance – emotionally, physically or mentally. The clues often lie in where that pain, tension or discomfort is felt. For example, feeling stiffness or pain in and around the neck region may indicate that perhaps we have rigid ideas or have become blinkered in our way of looking at life. Or it could mean that we are just feeling that everything is literally a pain in the neck!

Modelling Rent a Tent!

One of my earlier careers was modelling plus-size clothes, which I thoroughly enjoyed, especially as I didn't have to be wafer thin or 6 feet tall to do it! In fact, this was one of the first times in my life that I really experienced feeling confidence in my body and the sheer freedom this brought. However, I remember a time just before

I was due to model in a very prestigious 'runway' show for Harrods' exclusive plus-size department and was feeling nervous and anxious that all would go well. Although I was very excited about the show my enthusiasm had been dampened somewhat a couple of days before when a rather jealous friend remarked very cattily that Harrods must do a good line in 'rent a tents'! Her face dropped as I told her to look in *The Daily Telegraph* tomorrow as they were doing a feature on the clothes! However, I didn't feel as confident as I was making out and the day before the show I suffered extreme pain in my right knee and thought that I would be unable to walk, let alone model the clothes. I took painkillers, had physiotherapy and prayed that all would be well but minutes before the show was due to start the pain was still there – throbbing and hot. There was nothing else to do but go for it and hope that it would hold up and as I took my first step out onto the long white narrow walkway the pain went.

Pain in the knee area often relates to a fear of moving forward in your life and a need to stay secure and safe where you are – perhaps a resistance to change. This was so true of me. Stepping out onto the catwalk was a huge step in saying publicly, 'Here I am, this is me!' Looking back I feel that my knee pain reflected my own inner feelings of insecurity and vulnerability as I took a tentative step out into body and self-confidence. My body was literally communicating with me the instability I was feeling inside but once I had made the decision to step out and 'go for it' the pain subsided.

It was a fantastic show and so wonderful to see all these large, beautiful women confidently walking along that hallowed narrow strip which is usually only the domain of the supermodel.

But here we were – the super **plus** models boldly going where very few had gone before, each one of us putting our own body demons behind us as we sashayed our curves and danced into the moment!

Living in 'Tomorrow Town'

Up until that moment I (like so many others) lived in 'Tomorrow Town' and spent most of my waking moments in 'future think'. I denied my body, my shape and the way I felt about me. I spoke about all the things I would do when I had achieved the perfect body and the confidence I would have – I'd swim naked, make love on the beach, wear pink instead of black, flirt outrageously, present a television show, go horse riding, trekking in Nepal, and shopping without full make up on!

Living in tomorrow meant that I never noticed today – the moments of our lives that are passing by heedlessly as we breathe. I was so unaware of the magical moments and remember ruining what could have been a very romantic encounter as I sat in my (ex) boyfriend's car one night after an evening out. As he gazed lovingly into my eyes he suddenly became all choked up and moist-eyed as he whispered the words, 'Oh my pork chop [not the most romantic of all pet names but the feeling was there!], I do love you so much!' It was as if I had never heard him anyway as I automatically answered, 'Oh, you'll love me so much more when I'm skinny!' He replied that he couldn't love me anymore than he did right there in that moment. In a flash I had discounted his feelings, ignored his words, missed the moment and showed how little love, confidence or happiness I felt towards myself!

If you are one of the inhabitants of 'Tomorrow Town' just ask yourself how many more moments are you prepared to miss today whilst you are busy waiting for tomorrow to come?

Yesterday . . . All my Troubles Seemed so Far Away

Sam is a good friend of mine and whilst I was happy living in tomorrow he had retreated to yesterday. We made a good foil for each other, living in our own particular time warps, as we could forget about the present. You could tell Sam was a yesterday dweller as he used phrases like 'when I was,' 'If only I had done,' 'I really regret,' 'It's no use,' 'I've tried that already and it doesn't work,' etc. It's as if Sam was the original wearer of the seen it, done it, lived it and not doing it again because it's all so boring T shirt! I mention Sam here because he represents the growing number of men who are now becoming preoccupied with the way they look. In fact, in the cosmetic surgery stakes, men are rapidly catching up with women. The Dublin-based Harley Medical Group highlights that rhinoplasty (the nose op) has increased by 12 per cent over the past year, liposuction (fat removal) figures are up by 21 per cent and penile enlargement has taken a sizeable rise at 26 per cent! It seems that pressure to be perfect is working both ways and appears set to continue with the advent of so many more men's magazines and the emphasis on the 'dream boy' fantasy image.

It's no wonder that Sam prefers to live firmly in the past where he can be forever young, athletic and sport a fit, confident body. The Sam of today is older but in my eyes far more handsome than the boy of his past. His eyes are kind and full of his life's experiences, his voice is mellow and understanding. He's not a boy, he's a man and yet he prefers to linger somewhere between boyhood and becoming a young adult. It's as if he has the words 'It's hopeless, I can't change' stamped across his forehead as he defines himself by what he was and not who he is.

The Point of Power is NOW!

We all tend to drift between future states and past memories throughout our days – there is no problem in **planning** for tomorrow but it's when we begin to **live** in tomorrow that the danger comes. Owning your body means accepting your body, accepting you as you are right now – right at this very moment! In accepting who you are you begin to shift the power dynamics within your body and your mind. By accepting every part of you, you become yours. In becoming yours, you can change you, change the way you feel, act and think. How can you change something in you that was never really yours? If you space travel to tomorrow or are a ghost of your past then you never have today and today is where the magic happens and where the point of power lies.

How many times have you bought a dress or outfit that is a size smaller than you are because you hope it will motivate you to get into it? Usually what happens is the opposite. Every time you look at it there is a growing sense of despondency, as you still haven't managed to squeeze into it. Also, instead of enjoying wearing something that fits you now, you keep your life and body on hold waiting for tomorrow. Next time you are out shopping buy something you can wear and enjoy now!

A friend of mine wailed as she read this, saying, 'But that means I would have to buy a size 12 and there is no way I'm wearing a size 12 as I'm usually an 8 or 10!' Recently, she has put on a bit of weight and to everyone around her she still looks fabulous. But there is no way that she will admit to wearing or even buying a size or two bigger than the size she is used to. She identifies who she is by the clothes size she wears, which allows her no space for change physically, mentally or emotionally. The problem is that as her size 10s are on the tight side and she won't be seen dead in a size larger she has nothing to wear. Consequently, she feels 'depressed, daggy and dumpy' (to use her expressions). The more depressed she feels the less she cares about herself and the circle begins to get vicious! She finds herself drinking more, snacking at foods she doesn't really enjoy and being too tired to exercise, which she usually loves to do.

In refusing to be in her body as it is right now she is passing her days in a state of body despair. She hopes that no one will see her when she's out shopping and has begun to avoid going out at all. Her body and self-confidence are plummeting as she refuses to accept where she is at this point in her life.

Our bodies, minds and spirits are inextricably linked – what affects one will have an impact on the others and in my friend's case her life over the past few years has been emotionally upsetting for her. Her father died, work and finances have been insecure and she has had to take on several jobs to pay the bills, leaving her with little or no time for herself. Her mind and spirit are low and her body is sad. By denying where she is right now and how she is truly feeling she remains locked in a stalemate. Nothing will move or change until she can become the person she is and accept that this is how she is today. Once she can do this (even in a small way) she will begin to access her own unique body and self-power.

She said to me the other day that she just felt as if she was 'nothing' and wanted to know what she should do to change this. I suggested that if she felt she was 'nothing' then perhaps that was her answer. I wondered what being 'nothing' would feel like for her. To my amazement she smiled (a very small smile, but it was there) and said that actually 'nothing' felt quite good. She went on, 'I guess if I'm nothing I don't have to be anyone and no one can expect anything from me – because I'm nothing!' I nodded as she continued, 'And if I'm nothing then nothing matters which means that I matter coz I'm nothing!' Now she was really on a roll and I was finding it hard to keep up with the logic although it made perfect sense. 'Being nothing means I don't even have to be anything to myself, do I?' I smiled as I agreed with her and asked her what being nothing felt like. She answered, 'Free, it feels free – I feel free – there's nothing to do, nothing to think, nothing to feel, nothing to say.' She looked at me very seriously then and said positively, 'I am nothing!' There was a moment's silence and then we both began to giggle – an infectious bubble of a giggle that turned into raucous laughter as we both 'heard' what she had said.

By listening to her feelings of being nothing and staying with them my friend managed to free up her locked negative energy. Instead of trying to become 'something' she experienced the nothingness she felt and in so doing became everything in that moment. Later that week she had her hair done, bought a new top and a pair of 'wicked' trousers and felt freer than she had felt in a long time. In listening to and becoming aware of where she was in the present moment, she stopped trying to be where she wasn't and allowed her body, mind and spirit to create an entire new symphony – or as she described it, 'It's more like *The Rocky Horror Show*, *Grease* and *The Sound of Music* all rolled into one!'

Be where you are at this moment in time. Feel your feelings and try to stay with them instead of shutting them out or pushing them down. In being exactly where you are, you begin to connect with you. All too often we try to distract ourselves from our pain, fear, emotions and thoughts by diverting our attention away from ourselves. It's so easy to find ourselves heading for the fridge, putting on the TV or embarking on a shopping spree so that we can avoid actually meeting ourselves.

This is vital – this is the ultimate key to body and self-confidence. **We change by becoming more of who we are – not less.**

It's a great cosmic joke that so many of us feel that in order to change we must deny, deprive, restrict or rigidly discipline ourselves in some way or act in a manner which is at odds with whom we are. I remember trying to copy the way a girl at school walked because I thought that if I could walk like her I would become like her – she was really confident, bubbly and popular. She had a peculiar way of walking with her knees slightly bent all the time, and whilst it really suited her it looked utterly ridiculous on me and had my friends rolling with laughter as they spotted immediately what I was up to!

Live Your Life in the 'Now' Lane

I have found in my life and through my work as a body image therapist/counsellor and fitness presenter that the more I am me, fully and wholeheartedly, the more things drop into place. I laugh more, feel more confident and tend to stay centred in the present moment.

There is a theory in gestalt counselling known as the paradoxical theory of change, which echoes the above example:

> 'people change by becoming more fully themselves not by trying to make themselves be something or someone they are not.'
>
> **J Mackewn in *Developing Gestalt Counselling*, page 63**

When you give up struggling to be what you would like to become, when you allow yourself to be currently what you are now, at this moment in time, and become fully aware of who and what that is – you will change. There is a sparkling tingle of confidence you feel as you wear your body with pride and happiness. The greatest feeling about this is that no one can take it away from you. No one can pull you apart because you're on your own side. You are already backing the winning team! You support you! When you know your own truth, like and respect who you are and live your life in the 'Now' lane you have it all – because you **want** to be **you**!

> ### Dare to be You
> Come to the cliff, he said.
> They said, we are afraid.
> Come to the cliff, he said.
> They came.
> He pushed them.
> And they flew.
>   **Guillaume Apollinaire**

Take a risk; take a step closer to who you are. Every time you move to the edge of your awareness of what you really want, feel, think or believe you allow yourself to grow.

My sister, Helen, amazes me and has been such a guiding light for me as I have watched her move towards becoming the person she truly is. As a child she had an inner vision of how she saw and imagined herself to be. She described herself as a beautiful free spirit, slight and elfin with healing and artistic powers and a deep love of nature. She has always been drawn to the mysteries of the night sky and as a child she would spend hours lying on her bed just gazing up at the moon and the twinkling stars above her head.

As she grew up and became adult, she experienced so much pain as that vision became lost somewhere amongst people pushing her to conform to the ideals they had for her. She increasingly turned to drink, smoking and food as a way to soothe her battered feelings of trying so hard to become someone she was not. Disappointment after disappointment lowered her self-esteem as she took jobs that she was not particularly interested in. Helen's weight soared and her health deteriorated until she found that she was pregnant with her daughter Tannith and decided that she needed to begin to look after herself.

After giving birth to Tannith she allowed herself to reconnect with her childhood visions and the change in her over the years has been stunning. Her weight has melted away to reveal a tiny little delicate frame and she has stopped drinking and smoking. Her confidence and self-image are high and she structures her day to allow her the time she needs for creativity. She gets up at four in the morning to be at work for 5.00am, which means that her afternoons are spent at home drawing or walking in the nearby woods listening to the local wolves howl out their stories. She is in bed by nine after spending some time with her daughter and partner. A friend once asked her how she had managed to lose nearly five stone in weight, to which she replied that she didn't really know. It just ceased to be an issue – it was just a by-product of her becoming more creative, spiritual, being who she is and doing what she really wanted to do. She didn't try, she just was! It's as if one day she woke up and had become the vision she had always had. Every day she becomes more of who she is and whilst she still struggles with the more mundane parts of her life she now sees the stars again and knows that she can dance amongst them.

When the 'Doing' Stops the 'Being' Starts

Living in and accepting the body you have right now means that your body, mind and spirit begin to interconnect as one and there is an incredible sense of inner and outer harmony. Instead of spending your days fantasizing how good you will feel tomorrow, or how great you were yesterday, you begin to ask yourself the question, 'How can I make myself feel great right now – in this moment?' Living in the 'now' seems to be one of the hardest things for people to achieve as we are so conditioned to striving, perfecting, performing and succeeding that we tend to miss out on just being. Being where you are and who you are is the number one ingredient for living confidently in a body you respect and cherish.

Make Your Body Your Business

Living in the moment and being conscious of your body means that you become more aware of your needs and what is important to you. When you live as fully as you can 'now' you begin to recognize and act upon your priorities. So much of the time we put off things that we need to acknowledge or do for ourselves because someone or something else is taking our attention, energy or time. This can leave us with a continual feeling of unfinished business. You have to get your needs met – now!

This is the way many people experience their lives on a daily basis – they put off what they need to do for themselves and the longer the needs remain unmet, the more uncomfortable they become. It can be as simple as visiting the bathroom when you need to, or as difficult as ending a relationship you know isn't working for you anymore.

Ask yourself what you need to do right now? Are there things in your life that you are ignoring or putting off? Make your body your business and your life a priority. Begin to show yourself that you value and respect who you are and how you are.

A few weeks ago I had toothache. I put off doing anything about it, as it just wasn't convenient at the time. I took a painkiller and hoped that it would go away. It didn't, and eventually I had to seek help from the dentist who extracted it there and then. Voilà – no pain, no ache, no tooth!

I thought I might have learned my lesson not to procrastinate by my gall stone episode and I realized how easy it was to become unconscious and uncaring of my body again!

Awareness never stops – there will always be new needs, feelings and priorities in every new moment of your life. And whilst we may not be able to meet all of them all of the time we can show our bodies respect and love by acknowledging that they are there.

Change From Within – Crack the Body Code!

The traditional view of change is that, for the sake of conforming to a moral, family or cultural standard, you must do so by the process of willpower, determination and discipline. But as a friend of mine once said, 'There are times when willpower is not enough – when your body has had enough!' When you instinctively know that something is right for you, your body moves in the best direction to achieve that. But, if you try to do things that your body dislikes, you'll end up resenting it and not following through. And, the more you try to force yourself to do something you hate, the more conflict you create. Change happens by first accepting what it is you feel and who you are and then by understanding and showing compassion and kindness towards your self – mind, body and spirit.

We are so busy trying to fix the parts of us that we don't accept that we never hear the body's call to wisdom and understanding. It never strikes us that things don't need to be fixed – they just need to be understood. If we understood our bodies' uniquely healing messages we'd change.

Very often the part of us that causes us to suffer the most also has the potential to teach us the most about who we are. Rather than trying to understand our own particular body code we run screaming to the nearest plastic surgeon pointing to the offending part with cries of, 'Cut it off – get rid of it – it's ugly, it's gross, it's unattractive and I can't look at it any more!' Change 'fix me' to 'understand me' and you have one of the most powerful keys to unlocking your own personal body code.

Imagine you have a power cut and you are suddenly plunged into blackness. How do you cope with the darkness all around you? Do you scream, yell and kick out at it, demanding that it be brighter, or do you simply light a candle? Most of us would set about finding an alternative source of light. But the mind is a powerful force and if you were plunged into darkness with no light to hand, your mind could start playing tricks on you. It could play on all your fears and insecurities. And the more you dwell on those fears and insecurities, the more real they would become. This mental battle with yourself would eventually leave you exhausted.

It's the same with us – by fighting our bodies and our selves we set ourselves up for failure, fatigue and futility. When you light your own candle of awareness you see what's real, and you step out of the body gloom into a brighter world.

Begin to understand your body's own personal code and unique wisdom by observing how you are at any given moment. Don't judge or criticize, just watch with interest. Step back a little from you and notice when you feel tense, how you sit and talk, and the words you say. Become aware of where your body holds tension and the effect different people and life situations have on you. When are you most relaxed and happy? When are you most tense?

Does your body yearn for rest but you keep going until you are on the brink of exhaustion? Do you enjoy and like the food you eat? Does the company you keep stimulate you? What makes you buzz? What makes you angry? Connect with your mind, body and spirit by noticing everything about you. When you know who you are you can understand and be who you are, which is summed up simply by the Russian philosopher Gurdjieff: 'to know, to understand, to be'.

In these times of increased pressure to become the perfect person, we try to shape and remould our bodies to become comparable with what we see in the glossy magazines. Never mind the fact that maybe it's impossible for our bodies physically to be 5 feet 9 and a mere size 10! By comparing ourselves to what we think we should become we ignore the beauty we already possess and once more stop living in the moment while we fantasize about what tomorrow may bring.

It's a sad truth but much of the suffering seen by therapists is a result of their clients' perceptions that they are unable to shine as brilliantly as they perceive others to.

Allow yourself to shine from this moment on and accept that this is you: your body, your face, your shape, your eyes, your hands, your smile and your feelings. There is no one in the world like you – how can you compare yourself with anyone else?

Marianne Williamson puts it beautifully in her book *A Return to Love* (pages 190–1):

> Our deepest fear is not that we are inadequate. Our deepest fear is that we are powerful beyond measure. It is our light, not our darkness, that most frightens us. We ask ourselves, Who am I to be brilliant, gorgeous, talented, fabulous? Actually, who are you *not* to be? You are a child of God. Your playing small doesn't serve the world. There's nothing enlightened about shrinking so that other people won't feel insecure around you. We are all meant to shine, as children do. We were born to make manifest the glory of God that is within us. It's not just in some of us: it's in everyone. As we let our own light shine, we unconsciously give other people permission to do the same. As we're liberated from our own fear, our presence automatically liberates others.

Check In With Yourself

How often do you check in with yourself? Do you just take a minute to ask yourself how you feel about what is happening at that moment in your life? How many times do you stay somewhere you'd rather not be or spend time with people who drain your energy? Does your vocabulary consist of words like 'should', 'ought to', 'must' and 'it's my duty'? These words keep you locked into the future or the past – they control what you will do and to a greater extent how you will feel. When you do what you 'should', you are automatically conditioning yourself to respond in a pre-planned way. How many Christmases are ruined because people feel that they 'should' have aunty Maud, uncle Peter and cousin Jane over for the day? Tensions run high as everyone tries hard (perhaps too hard) to get along and find some area of common interest to talk about. Being bound by your word binds up your feelings and the chance to be fully present in the moment.

Change 'should' to 'could' and experience the fabulous choice that this gives you. You **could** have all your relatives over for Christmas, but (and here's the great bit) you don't have to! You **could** do anything that day – stay in bed drinking champagne and nibbling on your favourite delicacy, go to a mountain retreat, play endless games of scrabble, read a good book, have a party or a video fest, or just do whatever takes your fancy! Everything is open to you and keeps you centred in the present moment.

I *Could* Love my Body

When you apply the same way of thinking towards your body you give yourself the choice to feel amazing about being you! Saying that you **could** love your body opens you up to the possibility and sometimes that's all we need to get us started – a possibility, an opportunity to feel, think and act differently.

If you find yourself saying and thinking that you don't love your body, just take a moment to say, 'Ah, but I could,' then watch and see what happens! Loving your body is about being body conscious and body/self-aware, and the best way to achieve this is to constantly ask yourself how you are. So at different points throughout your day ask yourself this question: 'How am I?' If the answer is that you're happy and content with the way things are going then great – you are honouring and respecting your body and self in the moment and your needs are being met. If the answer is that perhaps you are feeling uncomfortable, tired, bored or aware of some sort of frustration, then ask yourself what it is you need. Sometimes you don't need to do anything but simply acknowledge the way you are feeling or the thoughts you have. Awareness brings change.

A client of mine (Linda) has a job which involves sitting through many long and drawn-out business meetings. She would love to have more confidence in herself and especially in her body but feels insignificant most of the time. She loves her job but finds the meetings tedious. She tried the technique of asking herself 'How am I?' in the middle of one such meeting and became aware that she was holding back thoughts that she really wanted to be able to express. The meetings were always so full of her colleagues' ideas and reviews that she realized that she always approached the meetings with a sense of being withdrawn and hardly ever put into words the ideas or suggestions which were in her mind. As such, she always felt that she wasn't really a part of what was going on and felt left out. She knew that her colleagues would be amazed if they knew how she felt as they valued her very much as part of the team.

But it wasn't about them; it was about her, and how she could change from feeling excluded to being included. In understanding why she always felt the meetings were tedious she could now change her approach to them. Before every meeting she began to rehearse and visualize herself taking a more active part. At first she found it hard to express her own views and concentrated on asking her colleagues to explain their visions and ideas in more detail. She openly began to agree or disagree with things that were being said and found that she actually began to enjoy the meetings more. Her business associates must have noticed this subtle change as they began to turn to her more for her opinion and comments. Gradually, Linda found the inner strength and confidence to voice new ideas that she had for the company, which were welcomed warmly.

In becoming aware of how she was feeling and by making one small change Linda made a huge shift in how she valued and related to her self. In asking one small question, 'How am I?' she opened up her feelings, thoughts and needs and began to live her life according to what was important to her. This one small change also had an amazing impact on her physical state of being. Usually at meetings she would sit kind of crunched up and hunched over. Her breathing would be constricted and she usually found that the tension she felt brought on a bad headache by the end of the day. Now when Linda was at meetings she noticed that she sat taller and leant forward into the table. Her shoulders were relaxed back and down instead of being held up by her ears and her breathing was freer and calmer.

Body States

Our thoughts, feelings and emotions affect our bodies on a second-to-second basis. Watch how someone sits or walks when they are feeling low or depressed. The very words 'low' and 'depressed' conjure up an image of someone with their head hung down, their shoulders rounded over and a posture that is slumped and heavy looking. Their body state is very negative. Equally, notice the difference when you see someone who is happy and excited. Their bodies are alive with an energy which makes them stand taller and move with ease. Their heads are lifted and they find it difficult not to smile!

Our thoughts, which are influenced by our beliefs, determine our feelings, which in turn affect our body state. These go round in a loop to affect our thoughts again. It's a never-ending circle, which can be used positively or negatively.

Body Blocks

One of my clients, Sue, always thought that she was ugly and had a complex about her teeth, which meant that she never smiled. She believed that she would never be as pretty as her older sister to whom she was always being compared. Thus, on meeting Sue for the first time, she kept her hand in front of her mouth as she spoke, which made it difficult to hear what was being said. To make matters worse, she would sit with her head forward so that her long hair fell over most of her face and she would hardly ever make eye contact. All of this clearly made her feel unconfident, uncomfortable and unsure, which fuelled her thoughts of not being attractive enough! And so it goes on – round and round until you step off the treadmill and into your life!

Working with Sue was incredibly powerful. During our sessions she really attempted not to cover her mouth whilst she spoke. The result was that at first she didn't say much at all but you could tell that she was feeling a huge amount. Removing her hand from her face meant that she no longer blocked her words and eventually after a few weeks her words began to tumble freely from her lips as if they had been finally let out of prison.

One change set into motion a series of changes and the Sue of today smiles and expresses herself with awareness and honesty as she creates a positive loop of confidence.

Become aware of how you block your body and prevent your energy from flowing freely. Do you sit hunched over or keep your arms folded across your stomach or chest area? Do you talk with your head down or find that you frown all the time? Are your clothes restrictive in any way? Do you walk in shoes that are fashionable but painful? Do you constantly eat foods that make you feel bloated or do exercise that you hate? Look at the ways you stop your own body energy from flowing.

One client would always sit with a cushion in front of her. It was comforting and protective at the same time and it also hid the part of her that she disliked the most. Now, she cuddles a cushion out of choice and awareness and not because she feels the need to hide.

Rich Body, Poor Body

Change your body state and your mental state will change, and vice versa. Change an unhelpful thought to one of kindness and you will open yourself up to an entire new way of being and feeling.

The next time you are feeling down, lacking in energy or just a bit low, imagine how you would be feeling if you had just been told that you had won a million pounds! You probably wouldn't just sit around moping, feeling all soggy and deflated, but would be energized into action! You might fantasize about what you could do with the money and remobilize all of your greatest dreams and longings into being. Your state would have changed in an instant – look around you, you're alive and anything is possible. Your body is your very own pleasure palace, ready to be enjoyed, loved and appreciated. You don't have to win a million to feel like a million. It's your choice – don't stay trapped in body poverty. Love the body you live in and begin to see how rich you really are!

Make it a Victorious Circle – Not a Vicious One!

Stop trying to break the vicious circle – just make it a victorious one instead! The circle is a very powerful symbol in its own right and implies a cycle or order of events, which will continually lead us back to where we are. In magic the circle offers protection, in sacred dances the circle is used to generate the feeling of unity and oneness; many children's games are played in circles to create bonding and friendship.

Use the power of the circle but change it from vicious to victorious and you have another powerful key to body love and confidence! When your thoughts are kind, helpful and accepting of you and you create new beliefs to back them up, your body responds accordingly and begins to move in a lighter, more harmonious way, freeing up any tension which in turn makes you feel better about yourself. Essentially, you are creating your own ring of confidence around you. You will find an exercise for creating your own victorious circle on page 244.

Sometimes it's not even necessary to do anything about what you feel or think – just becoming aware of it creates the space for your own inner power and confidence. Anthony De Mello, in his book *Awareness*, puts it simply: 'What you are aware of you are in control of; what you are not aware of is in control of you.'

NOW is the Only Moment you Have – Live it Well!

Imagine that this is your last day on earth – at the end of today you will no longer exist as yourself. This is it, the final outcome – all of your tomorrows have been and gone and you are left with only a few more minutes to live. Ask yourself these questions:

* ★ Did I enjoy my life?
* ★ Did I fulfil my purpose for being here?
* ★ Did I live in a body I accepted, loved and was proud of?
* ★ Did I experience living fully or just go through the motions pretending to be what everyone else wanted me to be?
* ★ Do I know myself better now than I did at the beginning?
* ★ Am I sad to be leaving this body, which has served me and loved me for the whole of my life?

If this truly was your last hour would you really spend your last minutes hating and criticizing your body or would you be trying to find some peace and acceptance within your self? Life is really too short to cheat yourself by not liking or loving your body and undervaluing yourself. It is by imagining our death that we begin to realize how fully alive we can be and put into perspective our lifelong hatred of our 'imperfect' body parts. How can you hate your nose when you'd give anything to be able to breathe for just a few minutes more? How can you loathe your legs when you'd do anything to be able to run towards another day? Criticizing your stomach is pointless, as you'd love to be able to enjoy your favourite food or drink for the last time! How can we hate our bodies when they do so much for us – when our entire lives are experienced through them?

I was so moved by a lady in one of my workshops as she welled up in tears, saying that if these were her last minutes she wouldn't be criticizing her flabby arms but thanking them for being able to hold her husband as she told him she loved him one final time.

Most of us go through our lives in denial of our own demise –

somehow we believe that we are eternal and have endless hours ahead of us. Physically, we are here in these bodies for such a short space of time – spiritually, we may go on forever.

The Body Beloved

My mum died over 12 years ago and I remember the day of her death and my thoughts as clearly as if it were yesterday. Two years before her death, she had suffered a massive stroke, which left her unable to walk or use the left side of her body at all (she didn't even know that she had a left side). It was a beautiful summer morning in July and I had popped in to see her in the nursing home. She wasn't feeling well that day and I gave her a kiss, told her I loved her and said that I would just have a quick chat with the Matron. I left the room for about ten minutes and when I returned she had died. As she gazed out at me with eyes that would never see my face again I found myself thinking, 'Is that it? Have you really said all the things you wanted to say? Hugged all the people you wanted to hug and done everything you ever wanted to do?' I wondered if she had loved her life and enjoyed living in her body and hoped that she had because it was all over so soon. In that moment it came home to me that there were no more chances to experience the joy and peace that a loved body can give you.

As my sister and I said prayers by her side she looked so small and ordinary and yet we both knew how extraordinary she was. This was the body that had given us life and these were the arms that had surrounded us in love. This was the body that collapsed in shock when her husband dropped dead aged 35 from a heart attack and that recovered enough to return to work to give us all that we wanted. And at the end, this was the body that didn't want to die and fought so hard to stay with us for two years after the stroke took away half of it.

How can you hate a body that gives you so much?

Look around you – we are all extraordinary! **Really** look at the people you see everyday on the street – tall, short, curvy, slim, relaxed, tense, dark, large, small, pale, old, bald, hard, wobbly and wondrous! Watch the way their muscles dance under their skin with every movement they make. Aren't we incredible? Just look at the wonderful diversity of the human race.

Body Secrets

Look into the gnarled old face of a 97-year-old woman and catch the sparkling eyes of a 16-year-old girl hidden between the folds of skin. Wonder about all the secrets that are hidden within her shape and what amazing stories her body has to tell.

Every **body** tells a story. The scar on the upper lip, the barely discernable limp, the stunning woman who gazes at the floor, the old man who carries the war with him wherever he walks, the teenager wearing a trendy bandana to hide where cancer has eaten away at her hair. Look around and see the everyday body miracles that we all take for granted. Marvel at the way our bodies protect us, support us, allow us to experience passion and pain and still keep going!

Imagine meeting Christopher Reeve (the actor who played Superman), not knowing that he had played the role of the handsome, unbelievably strong and powerful superhero character! You wouldn't realize that you were in fact looking at **the real** Superman – the man who fights for his life every day and refuses to give up on himself. He shines brighter than he ever did in a body that does more than the storybook character could ever hope to achieve!

I repeat – how can you hate a body that gives you so much?

Now, every time you catch a glimpse of yourself or look in the mirror and are tempted to criticize, judge or condemn – just stop a moment and think about your own body story and the fact that through all eternity no one will ever walk, talk, think, smile, dance or love exactly like you do. That makes you special – that makes you unique – that makes you who you are.

That makes you extraordinary!

5.

Body Lessons/Body **Trust**

> You dream kiss my sleep, support my every waking hour, love
> me without question, hold me close – sensuous, safe and
> warm. Without you I am nothing. I trust you with my life –
> you are my life. In my body I trust.
> **Loz-Ann McCarthy**

The Hidden Self

For years I hid behind my body and developed a larger-than-life
personality to hide the tiny, fragile mouse that quaked inside. The
more I rejected and despised me, the more rigid and defensive the
'exterior' me became. My body provided me with so many excuses,
so many ways in which I could stay hidden from myself. In fact,
dislike of my body gave me one great big gorgeous excuse not to
do anything, which went something like this:

 ★ 'I can't go out to that party tonight – I'm too fat!'
 ★ 'I'll never be a dancer – I'm too fat – might as well not
   bother.'
 ★ 'He will never look twice at me – I'm too fat and
   unattractive.'
 ★ 'I won't bother going shopping – I always look awful in
   anything I wear – what's the point – I'm too fat!'
 ★ 'I won't join that evening class – everyone will laugh at me
   – I'm too fat!'

Sounds like a stuck record doesn't it?

My fat gave me good excuses to keep hidden the parts of me that I found hard to express or deal with. My fat was my biggest lie and kept the 'real' me safely locked up inside where no one could get to me – a place where I didn't have to communicate my needs, fears or dreams.

I remember being surprised years ago by a lady who was a regular at my aerobics classes who asked me if I ever had a bad day or felt depressed. She went on, 'I just can't imagine that you ever get angry, cry or feel upset!'

That was because I always suppressed my feelings so that they became consumed by my body and not expressed in the moment.

Her words really amazed me as I realized that the image I put across was always one of forced happiness. It certainly wasn't what I felt inside and she would have been shocked to see the Astrid that cried, binged and stayed in bed for days because she was too depressed about her life to get up.

I found an old diary entry, which reads:

> I didn't get out of bed today, my stomach hurt too much for me to walk very far. My bedroom's dark and smells of stale food. Under my bed are the remains of half-eaten food; sandwiches, dried up spaghetti soaked in rancid butter, family size bars of chocolate, cheese and mouldy bread.
>
> I couldn't stop eating today; it was one long endless binge. It started last night and I knew that today would be a wash out even though I told myself that today I would be good, today I would begin again. Today was Monday. New diets always start on Monday!
>
> I hate myself for being like this, I feel sick and my stomach hurts so much. I can't go on like this; I know I have to change. I must stop doing this to myself – but I can't stop! I am out of control again. Helen [my sister] looked at me in disgust when she found me still in bed at 5.00pm. I told her I was ill. It's not a lie – I AM ILL. I hate having to make excuses for myself. No one knows how I feel.

This was just one entry out of hundreds and they all said the same things again and again. How I would be good, how I would be thin, how I would begin again tomorrow, how I would live and all the things I would do when I was 'perfect', when I was in control!

When people commented on how they perceived me to be they missed the secret language which was running along parallel. Thus, when someone remarked that I was so funny, inside I was just desperate to be liked. My 'great personality' washed over my wounds and my constant smile silenced the screaming inside! Someone once said that I was the life and soul of the party but inside I felt like I was lying – I felt so flat. And when people remarked that I was a fun, lovable, outgoing, wonderfully happy girl – I was at the height of my bulimia!

Feeling low or negative about your body can keep you in hiding, not only from other people but also more importantly from yourself. Ask yourself if there are ways in which feeling negative about you keeps you hidden. Does your behaviour compensate for how you feel and, if so, in what ways? What is it that you are afraid of showing, becoming, doing, feeling or experiencing?

Valerie's Story

I met Valerie at one of my workshops. She told us that she was 72 years old and had lived a full life, raising three children, coping with work and the death of her husband after 25 years of marriage. She suffered from rheumatism in her fingers, which made holding things very difficult. She had been through countless problems and obstacles in her life and had overcome them all through her will and sheer determination. She was a success in so many ways and yet she felt like a complete and utter failure because the one 'problem' she had never been able to overcome was her weight. All her triumphs meant nothing as she still berated herself for being too fat.

In spite of all Valerie's achievements and successes, she could only see failure and at the age of 72 she was still locked in fighting with her body, hating and condemning herself for being one stone more than she wanted to be.

Your Body is Your Greatest Teacher

In Valerie's case her body and her weight were her greatest teachers. They provided the one lesson she most needed to learn – to love herself unconditionally. All of the other 'lessons' in her life were about coping, letting go, raising her children and endurance over immense physical pain. But she also needed to learn to love and nurture herself and make sure that her own needs were met and that her dreams were validated. This had always been the hardest thing for her to do until finally here she was in a 'Loving Your Body' workshop, still trying to understand how to love herself.

As she shared her story with us she looked around rather wistfully at all of the younger people there and said, 'Don't wait until you're 72 or older to love who you are – do it now while you still have years of body love ahead of you!'

Valerie is still working on understanding her body's messages and recognizes that this will probably be the most difficult thing she has yet had to face.

Your body's syllabus is varied and tough and it challenges you to turn all of your ideas and thoughts about YOU upside down! The body lesson to be learnt is to see yourself as you are, and then learn to love what you see and develop a high self-esteem. It asks you to communicate your dreams, visions, needs and innermost desires and it has a timetable, which can last your whole life long.

Body Combat

Remember, what we focus on we have more of – so the more you hate or dislike any part of your body, the more pain and frustration you will experience and the more you will become locked in body combat! In loathing my size and myself, I held my fat and pain all the closer to me as my eating became more and more out of control. In my mind the thought of loving or even liking and accepting myself was anathema to me. I could only love myself when I was thin – when I deserved loving, when I had beaten the 'enemy' – fat! My self-esteem and self-worth were so low that I thought I had no right to be loved, successful or happy as a fat person. In my mind those three things just didn't go together.

Feel Your Body and Love it Anyway!

My personal lesson has been to feel and accept my body and love it anyway. At one time I thought that my best friend (food) lived in the fridge – always there to provide me with that instant comfort and reassurance that I so needed. I now know that my greatest teacher and ally was my fat – it taught me the lessons I so needed to learn. It taught me to love me in spite of me. It asked me to love and look after something that I wanted to run away and hide from. But we can't run away from ourselves – every lump, bump, freckle and dimple is a part of us and in denying our bodies we deny who we are.

My fat gently surrounded me with its warm, soft, loving layers of protection and whilst I screamed torrents of abuse at it, my fat was there to show me how to love the person I was. In essence, my fat showed me how to come to terms with myself regardless of what I looked or felt like. It taught me how to go beyond the limitations of destructive negative thinking and begin my own unique journey from body hate to body love and freedom.

I realized that I had created my fat and excess weight in order for me to learn, grow, transcend and move on. It's as if I had decided that on some deeper, spiritual level this was the best way for me to change and evolve. I would never have become the person I am today without the lessons that my fat has taught me. This book would have never been written and my career would never have happened in the way it has if my fat had not shown me how to love my body.

I had 'fat' as my teacher. Other people may learn their body lessons through their skin, eyesight, height, shape, weight, hearing, health, ability or disability, etc. The parts of you that you reject or that cause you suffering are usually the areas which will bring you the most learning and, ultimately, joy.

This is phenomenal – realizing that your body can be your friend, teacher or healer creates a huge shift in how you see, treat and understand yourself.

Body Expectations

We all make our own choices about how we treat our bodies every day of our lives, whether that treatment is based on love and acceptance or on hate, denial or something that we lack within ourselves. Many people feel that by accepting our bodies we stop caring about them but the reverse is true. By accepting our bodies and ourselves, we care more!

When we make choices based on extreme care for who we are and how we wish to feel, we are making those choices with love and compassion for ourselves.

But, when we make choices based on negativity or body fear, our expectations are incredibly high as we hope our new and improved nose, ears, brows, lips or thighs will bring us total confidence, and that we will automatically feel superb about ourselves. If this doesn't happen then we may seek out more surgery or go on an even more restricted and nutritionally deficient diet, and so the body/soul searching never stops. **Whenever body love is based on body looks we are in danger.** Whenever you have surgery out of hate, you wound your body, mind and spirit and the scars run deep. Whenever a diet leaves you empty and malnourished you are not only starving your body, but your soul too! Any exercise regime that literally whips you into shape hurts right to the core, as your body knows that you must hate it to hurt it so much.

The Body Betrayed?

I have a friend who is totally happy with her body and loves herself for who she is. She has been fighting the 'body war' for most of her life and has finally agreed a truce, except for one area – her ears. She wants an operation to pin back her ears and says jokingly that Dumbo has nothing on her!

This area remains a source of conflict for her, in that while she accepts, loves and thinks kindly of her ears, she still wants them changed. She genuinely feels that she will look better with them pinned back and that this will give her more confidence. She decided to wait a year before doing anything about them, during which time she became aware that her ears had very little negative effect on her confidence and life. She realized that she loved every part of her, including her ears, but that she still wanted surgery. This was now causing the most conflict within her. She said to me, 'I feel in such a dilemma because if I love and accept my ears I shouldn't feel the need to change them. I feel like I am betraying myself after all the time I have spent on learning how to love myself.'

She decided that as she still felt uncertain she would wait a further six months before doing anything. After six months she said that she had decided to go ahead and have the surgery. She explained, 'I am approaching the surgery through a place of deep love and understanding about myself. I know that pinning my ears back will make no difference to how I feel about them or me. It's a choice I have made through really loving my body and wanting the best for me – this is something I want.'

In that moment she ended her conflict and sense of body betrayal.

She knew that having her ears pinned back would make no difference to the love and confidence she felt towards her body but that she would prefer it if they didn't stick out so far. Her choice was made through awareness, love and a deep sense of honesty about who she is.

Body Changes

Each one of us is free to make changes to our bodies if we so wish and it is certainly not my place to comment on individual diets, or cosmetic or surgical procedures. All I would say is, look very carefully at how you approach the change you may be thinking of making. When you seek change out of hate, dislike or contempt for your body or self, you perpetuate the problem. It's like taking painkillers for toothache – it can alleviate the pain you feel but the underlying cause of that suffering is still there, and sooner or later it will need to be addressed.

One of my clients, Mandy, underwent liposuction on her thighs and had a tummy tuck at the same time. Mandy is bulimic. As you might imagine the surgery made no impact on her mind and the bulimia is worse than ever. Today, Mandy is lost somewhere deep within her own world of body hate while she rages at a body that will never be good enough or shape up to the body of her dreams.

When you make changes to your body make sure that they are made out of respect, care and love for the person you are. If you choose to go on a diet, make sure it supports you physically and emotionally. Make sure that the foods you eat make your body hum with pleasure. If you decide to exercise, do something that you love. There's no point in doing aerobics or going to the gym if you spend every minute hating it! Don't lie to your body by forcing it to do what it 'should' – be real, be more aware of who you are and make choices born out of love not loathing!

Designer Bodies!

Have you seen the BBC programme *Changing Rooms*? I love it! It's a simple but effective concept as two neighbours or friends are given carte blanche to go into each other's houses and redesign one room which is in need of some repair or attention. They each set off with a professional designer in tow and that's where the fun begins. Although they might think that they know what their neighbour will like, it's a hit and miss affair as they go about redecorating. They are limited to a small budget and arguments abound as the designers (like TV magicians), pull swags, tails, feathers, pots of startling colours and gothic beds made out of MDF out of their designer hats! Looks of terror appear, as both sides are unsure if their designs will work or be appreciated by the other party.

After two days of hard work the moment of truth arrives as each couple goes back to their respective homes to see the results. Breath is held as everyone waits for the reaction – will they like it or hate it? It's a gamble, and whilst on occasion the results may be pleasing, the initial response is usually one of shock!

Whenever we allow someone else to dictate what we eat, how we exercise or how we 'should' look, it's as if we are playing our own risky game of *Changing Rooms*, only this time it's called *Changing Bodies*! Would you really allow your neighbour to decide what was right for you? Many of us do exactly that as we follow some crazy eating plan which consists only of boiled eggs, or embark on the latest fitness trend because we are told it will burn fat from our buttocks!

A friend of mine went to see a top UK nutritionist who had some new way of prescribing the foods you should eat based on your body alignment, posture and height. This woman had successfully helped several top celebrities shed some unwanted pounds and my friend hoped the same thing would happen for her. However, after an initial drop in weight her body stubbornly refused to drop anymore. Every time she returned to the clinic she was told that she must stick to the programme and keep doing more of the same – never mind that more of the same was driving her potty! When she voiced her concerns she was told that she must comply with the diet that had been given to her. Several months later and no lighter, she gave up.

Whilst one programme may work for some people it most certainly does not work for all people. Deep down, you already know what works for you, you just need to tune in and listen to your own body's wisdom. Subconsciously, my friend already knows what she needs to do to lose weight and her body reflected this by refusing to budge an inch further under the restrictive diet she was on.

My friend's experience mirrors what happens to so many of us when we hand over responsibility for ourselves by allowing someone else to dictate our eating patterns, exercise regimes, fashion sense and even what jobs we do. We all have the answers to what makes us happy, fulfilled or excited. We just need to ask ourselves the questions and then be daring enough to listen and respond to the answers. In my role as a psychotherapist I have found that if I listen to my clients for long enough they will tell me what's wrong. If I listen a little longer they will tell me how they can fix it.

Body By Me!

Back in the eighties, when aerobics was synonymous with high-cut leotards and multi-coloured leg warmers, there was a very charismatic instructor at the studio where I taught who was beloved by all of the women. He would prowl around the studio like some slinky black cat as he purred his way amongst the women growling out his instructions. 'Bend, stretch, reach – come on ladies you can give me better than that!' The women had sweat on their sweat as they pounded their bodies to the frenetic high-energy club beat. His classes were fun and always charged with a high degree of sexual energy, which he capitalized on by designing his own T shirt to advertise his classes, which read, 'BODY BY GEORGE'!

It always made me smile when I saw the studio full of women whose bodies had all been designed by George! Talk about the ultimate in handing over responsibility for how we looked! I longed to go and create the alternative version, which would read (as we proudly displayed our bosoms to the world) 'BODY BY ME!'

Beauty and the Beast!

Denise was a model – 24 years old and at the height of her beauty and radiance. She was mainly booked for close-up beauty shots as she had the most perfect flawless skin you could imagine. One evening after a particularly tiring day she came home to her apartment and began to run a bath. As she was waiting for the tub to fill up she treated her body to a relaxing massage using rich exotic oil she had bought earlier in the week. Allowing the oil to sink deep into her skin she walked to the sitting room and lit up a cigarette. Within seconds her body was alight and she desperately ran to the bathroom to try to douse her burning skin – her life had changed forever.

Denise suffered second-degree burns, which covered a third of her body and half of her face. She had reconstructive surgery on her mouth but still finds it hard to speak clearly or eat properly.

Denise is beautiful. She spoke out at a recent seminar saying, 'Confidence is the most beautiful thing in the world and no matter what you look like you can achieve anything you want – having confidence makes you beautiful!'

I was stunned to hear how much her life had changed and how she had coped. She smiled as she told us that one of the things she most wanted in her life was to be married and have a child. After the accident she had thought that this would never ever happen and yet she had met the man of her dreams a year after she was burned and is now seven months pregnant with their first child.

If you had told her that this was the way her life would unfold she would never have believed you. She laughed gently as she remembered her favourite childhood fairytale, *Beauty and the Beast*, and said that she knew what it felt like to be both. She went on, 'But that's okay – isn't there a bit of beauty and the beast in all of us?'

Denise is an inspiration. She accepts what has happened and who she is today. She says 'YES' to her life, her body and her self, as she looks at her appearance with a new light of understanding.

She told me that meeting her husband, Frank, was an amazing experience as here was a man who thought she was beautiful from the moment they first met. She told me, 'He didn't seem to see my scars or notice my leathery skin – he just responded to me as a person.' She continued, 'He always tells me I'm beautiful and I think I'm probably more beautiful now than when I was "perfect" as a model!'

Every one of us chooses different ways to learn how to become more of who we are and how to understand, love and look after ourselves in this life. You may know people who have alcohol or drugs as their teachers, or people who have issues with money, or sex, or are workaholics. All of our greatest pains, fears, addictions or worries are our most valued teachers and it is up to us to learn the lessons they bring. Denise learnt how beautiful she truly was, as her outer appearance changed beyond recognition. Day by day she had to learn to live in a body which didn't move so well, hurt in places and bore no resemblance to the former Denise. And, more incredibly, she learnt how to love this new image and be confident and proud of who she had become.

Body Lessons

To begin to understand what your own body's lessons are, ask yourself what it is about your body you dislike, and how this non-acceptance affects your life. What are all the payoffs you get (either positive or negative) from not loving you?

Everything we do in our lives has some kind of a payoff (something we get out of doing, living or behaving in certain ways). What does feeling bad about your body give you? Is it a distraction for not living your dreams? Does it provide you with an excuse for not participating fully in your own life? Or are you afraid of how fantastic you could be if you loved and felt great about you? That can be a scary thought. How happy **could** you be? Imagine living in a body that you treated well, loved and didn't complain about or criticize. Imagine what it would feel like not to have to hide behind years of body shame, disgust, fear or denial! Imagine looking in the mirror and winking instead of frowning – imagine loving the skin you're in! How can you ever fully experience your life in a body which feels wounded and unloved?

Body Trust

Earlier this year a friend of mine died. She was 32 years old and had been given five months to live. She was suffering from a particularly aggressive form of cancer, which had spread into her lungs. As the treatments took every last bit of strength from her shrinking body she stayed loving and looking after herself and her body until the last moment. She had always treated her body with love – she ate healthily, never smoked or drank alcohol and loved to go out walking. She looked the perfect picture of health and vitality. So good, in fact, that the doctor commented that she was the healthiest looking sick person he had ever seen!

A friend of hers raged against her imminent death, asking her why she didn't hate her body. After all she had done to love herself, her body had let her down and she was going to die! She replied that she was so much more than her body. Her body was where her soul found expression and her higher self called her to live out her dreams.

Right up until the end of her life she continued to love and trust what was happening to her. She believed that every time we confront some intense difficulty, we know there is something we haven't learned yet, and that the universe is now giving us the opportunity to learn. She totally trusted that her body was now giving her the ultimate challenge to say 'Yes' to her death as she had done so wholeheartedly to her life!

Body trust is seeing beyond your physical form into a place where your higher self loves you unconditionally. It is about accepting your place in the universe and feeling safe within your body, even when that body is ill, crumbling or dying.

Thank Your Body

Part of learning to love and have confidence in your body is beginning to thank your body for all that it has done for you. Just acknowledge all the wonderful things your body does for you on a day-to-day basis. Even when you are asleep your body goes on working to keep you safe and protected, alerting you to the slightest noise or discomfort.

Become aware of all the ways your body works for you, endlessly giving you what you want. It always tries to maintain your optimum health and well-being in spite of what we may do to it. When we drink too much our bodies work overtime to eliminate the toxins. When we cut or injure ourselves our antibodies fly into action to help heal the wound. When we are too tired, run down or exhausted, our bodies will make us stop so that we can rest, heal and recuperate. We need to listen to our own body wisdom and thank ourselves for being exactly who we are.

In thanking my body I began to accept me and gradually found myself doing all the things that I had previously shied away from or had never allowed myself to experience before. I realized that it was not my weight that had stopped me, but my attitude to it. The only barriers were the ones that I had created in my own mind.

Thanking your body allows an inner shift to take place and a gentle healing to begin. I was very moved by this testimonial to her body from a client of some years ago. She wrote:

> Today, my fat is leaving my body. My weight has been dropping slowly over a period of time and my shape is changing as I watch.
>
> I'm not dieting, exercising madly or even particularly desiring the weight to go. It can stay or leave – either way is okay with me. But as I watch my fat disappear I have to confess that there's a sense of sadness as I feel that I am saying goodbye to an old friend. A friend who took all the insults and the punishments and constant dreadful abuse and always loved

me back – unconditionally and universally. Someone who was always there to protect and support me, keeping me safe and hidden until I was ready to accept the whole of me and love me unconditionally. All I can say as I watch my fat leave my body is thank you. Thank you so much for being there!

The Wonder of You

Have you ever been so overwhelmed with the beauty of something – a sunset, a child's first smile, or a flower – that you were filled with a sense of abundance and wonder? Have you ever walked along a deserted beach at dusk and felt the stirrings of sand take you back to ancient times? Have you ever cried tears of joy as a character in a movie overcomes huge obstacles and gets to live again? Have you ever experienced the ghostly tingling down your spine as you listen to a haunting melody, which seems to tug at your very soul?

There is a school of thought that believes that all these experiences come from your spirit, which encompasses the higher self. This is the part of us that sees beyond the world of the petty and transports us into a blissful, loving space. This is the part that sees someone's pain behind the screaming anger, the fear behind the defences and the beauty behind the rage. Essentially, it is the part that calls you to look in the mirror and see the depths of beauty in your own eyes and not the wrinkles around them. It is the part of you that loves who you are unconditionally and continually lifts you up to see the wonder of you.

When you look at your stomach and remember the joyful birth of your first child instead of criticizing the stretch marks, when you spot a new wrinkle and smile instead of frown, when you stroke your skin with love instead of revulsion, when you know that age can take nothing away from you because your beauty is timeless: that's when you will experience the wonder of you!

Body Happiness

When you suffer over any part of your body it is a sign that you are out of touch with the truth; the truth about who you are. Suffering occurs when we identify ourselves with some kind of false image, which we feel we have to become in order to be accepted, loved, admired, sought after or recognized. Consequently, we identify with what that image means and find ourselves in pain whenever we don't match up. Just as physical pain occurs to make you understand there is illness or disease, suffering points out that there is an untruth somewhere as your body illusions clash with your reality. Suffering will always lead you to an area where you have not yet grown, where you need to evolve, transform and change.

To experience joy and happiness with and in your body you don't need to acquire or add anything – you've got to drop something instead. Drop the illusions you have about your body and how having bigger/smaller breasts, a new nose, liposculpted thighs or a tiny bottom will make you happier. The truth is that they might and they might not. If you think that having bigger breasts will turn you into a sex goddess and they don't, then what are you left with? If you identify with and place your happiness on an external image you will always be left wanting because that image changes – ultimately beauty is transitory. What happens when that image changes and you desire smaller breasts? More surgery? More pain? More unhappiness? When who you are is not dependent on how you look – when you no longer define or identify yourself by a passing image, you open yourself up to experience true happiness.

Anthony De Mello puts it beautifully in his book *Awareness* (page 106):

> I'm not beautiful because everyone says I'm beautiful. I'm really neither beautiful nor ugly. These are things that come and go. I could be transformed into a very ugly creature tomorrow, but it is still 'I'. Then, say, I get plastic surgery and I become beautiful again. Does the 'I' really become beautiful?

We are so much more than our bodies, jobs, likes, dislikes, hobbies, houses, etc. We are spirits expressing our callings in physical form.

I used to base my entire identity on being fat and what fat meant to me. In my mind fat was something that was ugly, revolting and made you an unworthy person. In saying that I was fat I was also saying that I was ugly, revolting and unworthy! One of my greatest and most liberating lessons was to stop identifying with being fat. I changed 'I'm fat' to 'I have fat' and suddenly my whole world opened up! I became more than my weight. I began to notice other attributes of mine that had previously always been swamped by my identification with fat. I became someone who was creative, lovable, strong, energetic, fit and healthy. I also happened to have fat – so what? My fat no longer had the power to make me feel disgusting and as I stopped thinking of myself as a fat person and saw myself as a person who carried extra fat, I became separate from it. I began to see me for who I really was and was no longer bound by my own restrictive limitations.

A client of mine would always say that she was depressed. She identified the person she was in terms of how she felt. She tried changing 'I'm depressed' to 'I have depression', or 'depression is there' and was able to take a step back from feeling immersed in depression to allowing herself to experience it and then permitting the feeling to pass.

It is exactly the same with anorexia, bulimia, alcoholism or any other experience, addiction or behavioural patterns you identify with. When you don't identify with what you are suffering from, you create the space to see the truth about who you are.

Julie came to see me. She was suffering from anorexia – her first words to me were 'I'm anorexic'. She was really shaken when I asked her what else she was. She said, 'Don't you want to talk about my anorexia?' I replied that as she had just told me she was anorexic I knew one thing about her and that I would like to know other things about her too. She was absolutely silent for what seemed like hours as she desperately searched herself to come up with answers. Towards the end of our first session she broke down in tears saying, 'I've been anorexic for 13 years and whenever people find out they just shake their heads with a knowing "Ah" as if they know all about me – as if being anorexic sums me up. No one has ever asked me what **else** I am!'

Julie began a tentative journey to find out about all the other amazing and fascinating aspects of her, which had been hidden for years under the ever-tightening belt of anorexia. And, whilst she explored her anorexia she began to change 'I'm anorexic' to 'I have anorexia'. Today, Julie still struggles but she has created space between herself and her anorexia. She is no longer consumed by the 'dis-ease' as she begins to understand who she really is.

I love this extract from pages 14, 15 and 16 of *The Velveteen Rabbit* by Margery Williams. Two toys in the nursery (the skin horse and the rabbit) are talking about becoming real.

'Does it hurt?' asked the rabbit.

'Sometimes,' said the skin horse, for he was always truthful. 'When you are Real, you don't mind being hurt.'

'Does it happen all at once, like being wound up,' he asked, 'or bit by bit?'

'It doesn't happen all at once,' said the skin horse. 'You become. It takes a long time. That's why it doesn't often happen to people who break easily, or have sharp edges, or who have to be carefully kept. Generally, by the time you are Real, most of your hair has been loved off, and your eyes drop out and you get loose in the joints and very shabby. But these things don't matter at all, because once you are Real you can't be ugly, except to people who don't understand.'

6.
Body Hurt

Maybe

When there's no more surgery
When we've lifted our faces more times than we can
remember
Liposucked away our thighs
Botoxed our brows
And plumped collagen into our lips

When we've reshaped our breasts
Defined our muscles, had a rib removed and our teeth
bleached white and realigned

When we've suffered the last diet
Sweated out the final pound
And erased all our wrinkles

Maybe then –
When there's nowhere left to go on the outside –
We will look inside
And see how beautiful we really are!

Astrid Longhurst

Body Rage!

Forget road rage – it's body rage that's the real danger!

'Emma'

Emma weighs 7 stone 3 pounds and wants to be everything to everyone's tastes – the ultimate pinnacle of gorgeousness! Emma hates her body with a vengeance and says that her proportions are all wrong! She wants bigger boobs, smaller hips, a flatter stomach and a perkier bum. Her life consists of eating, throwing up and sleeping. She has no friends and says that if she has a spare ten minutes she will throw up – just to clean out her stomach!

She says that her body is vile, disgusting and horrible. The backs of her hands are blistered and scarred from where her teeth have rubbed when she's been forcing her fingers as far down her throat as possible.

Her partner would love to have dinner parties and be a part of a social eating group but knows that they can't eat outside of their house! Emma has to colour-coordinate her food and puts into her stomach only foods that are of a neutral colour. Anything that is too pink, too red or too green doesn't get eaten.

I asked if she was concerned about her health and Emma told me, 'Health doesn't matter! I'll endanger that to be thin – it's really not an issue and if I die as a result of it – well that's it, it's happened! Sometimes I think I'll be too fat to die – God, just imagine me on a mortuary slab – they won't be able to find anything big enough to cover me up and they'll be thinking she's so fat! That's a horrendous thought. Sometimes I think Oh God, I can't die – I'm too fat to die.'

Emma is beautiful! She's petite, graceful, intelligent and overflowing with body rage!

'Sadie'

The first thing Sadie sees on her bedroom wall when she wakes up are the words 'FAT BITCH!'

She smiles engagingly at me as she says, 'Just in case I should forget for one moment that that is what I am!'

Sadie is 45, weighs 10 stone, is 5 feet 8 inches tall and is a sales manager with a thriving company.

She smiles all the time as she tells me, 'I shouldn't eat – I should be a size 6. If people see me eating they'll think I'm greedy and that it's no wonder I look like this! I don't want people to see me – it's bad enough that I have to see me! I'm so ashamed of eating!'

As we talk, Sadie is standing in front of a mirror glaring at her body as she tries to pull enough flesh together to make her point! She doesn't even notice as her skin turns red beneath the cruel pinches of her fingers. She turns to me and smiles broadly as she says, 'I wish I was just bones and skin – no ugly rolls, no clumpy white fat-ridden thighs, no disgusting wobbly flesh!'

Sadie has cut herself off from her friends and dreams about losing two stones. I ask her what this would mean to her and she seems confused as to exactly what it **does** mean. She replies vaguely, 'I can do something – anything – if I lose weight.' Her partner is the victim of her body rage as she screams abuse at him whenever he gently suggests that she needs to eat something. Sadie is about to undergo liposuction on her back, hips, upper and lower stomach and inner thighs. Her partner is distraught as he looks lovingly at her and says, 'I think it's totally uncalled for – I think she's brilliant the way she is. It's just not necessary – she's a babe!' As we talk he shows me photographs where Sadie has scribbled herself out in thick black ink. He looks so sad as he shows me a photo which he painstakingly stuck back together after she tore it up in a fit of body rage. It's a lovely photo of them both on holiday – they are smiling, sun kissed and look so together in their happiness. He loves that photo – she hates it and says it makes her look fat.

Sadie is blonde, beautiful, tormented and hides her pain behind a fixed smile! The only things that give her suffering away are the fine scars on the inside of her arm where she cuts herself to remind her not to eat all those 'dirty calories' which make her fat! Her scars on the outside tell us of the scars inside as she continues to be consumed by body rage.

'Sumara'

Sumara has just come out of surgery – it's her second fat removal operation in a year and she's groggy and in pain. Her mother stands by her side watching with concern as her daughter says shakily, 'I can't go through this again.' Sumara is a beautiful Asian woman with a body shape that reflects her heritage. She despises it and wants to look more European with slimmer hips and contoured thighs. The surgeon is happy with the results of this operation as he proudly informs her that he got six litres of fat out of her buttocks and inner thigh area. Sumara recoils as he hands her a jar full of liquefied yellowy, reddish, congealed sludge and she looks away in disgust.

Sumara's mother can't understand why her daughter wants to reject her race and culture. She believes that she is doing it because she so desperately wants to be a part of a stereotypical society and culture.

Two months later Sumara is out with a group of friends – both Asian and European. She asks them if they can see the difference in her legs and they say that they think her legs do look better, although they thought she was just fine as she was before. They love her for being Sumara – not for her legs! As the evening goes on Sumara drinks and eats to excess until one friend asks if she is worried about the fat coming back. Sumara replies, 'It doesn't matter – I can always get it sucked out again!' Eight months later Sumara is contemplating her third fat removal surgery.

Body Torture – the Anger Inside!

All these women suffer from what I call 'body rage'. This is an insidious 'dis-ease' that is sweeping the western world as more and more people lose touch with their bodies and treat themselves with less respect, care and love than ever before. These are perhaps extreme cases in that they all hate their bodies so much their lives are tortured because of it. However, whenever we find ourselves not truly living our lives to the fullest because our thoughts are preoccupied with how we look, we too are victims of body hurt and may suffer from body rage.

Body rage, like road rage, may be experienced in a mild form or one that leads you into a head-on collision! Just as people experiencing road rage use their vehicles as weapons to express their anger and frustration, those suffering from body rage turn their bodies into attacking missiles of pain, which are targeted to attack themselves.

A survey by *Top Santé* magazine (September 2001) highlighted that three-quarters of the women polled confessed to thinking about their bodies every day and the news is not good. When it comes to liking individual body parts:

- ★ 81 per cent are unhappy with their hips and thighs
- ★ 71 per cent dislike their bottoms
- ★ 62 per cent are unhappy about the size of their waist
- ★ 56 per cent hate their legs
- ★ 47 per cent are disappointed with their arms
- ★ 46 per cent are unhappy with their breasts

How sad that so many of us are living in bodies that continually bring dissatisfaction and disappointment instead of joy and happiness. How pointless that so many beautiful and vibrant women feel that their lives are ruled by the size and shape of a single body part, leaving them with no confidence and a pervading feeling that somehow they don't fit in.

A report entitled 'The Body and Self-Esteem', in issue 1 of the Body Shop magazine *Full Voice*, showed that the UK now has over 3.5 million anorexics and bulimics. What is more difficult to come to terms with is how these eating-distress conditions have become an accepted ritual in society. The starving skeletal frame of a person suffering with anorexia or the binge-purge behaviour of the bulimic no longer shocks us, as we fail to understand the massive impact these conditions have on people's lives.

Stop Using Food as a Weapon!

However, whilst anorexia and bulimia may be the extreme ends of the eating-distress condition, there are myriad eating disorders in between these two poles. Many women today find themselves hovering somewhere between these two conditions as food takes on a greater significance than ever before.

Yvonne (a client) explained her feelings about food as she said, 'I wish that I **was** anorexic or bulimic – then, maybe people would understand. But, I'm not! I'm not a compulsive or secret eater and I don't eat emotionally, but I know that something is wrong with my relationship with food. I don't enjoy eating any more and there's a niggling sense of guilt when I consume certain foods. I just don't feel that I eat "normally" any more.'

As our bodies have become more and more important, what we put into them has also become a high priority, with endless new diets and eating plans showing us why, what and how to eat. Never before have so many of us been so confused as we search desperately for the Holy Grail of thinness and seize upon anything that even vaguely resembles it (even though it may bear false promises). As we lose touch with our bodies we fear anything which may make them less than 'perfect' and a deep distrust sets in as we eye our food warily with suspicion. Our dinner plates become battlegrounds of willpower, manipulation and control, and war begins each time we open our mouths.

To Consume or Not to Consume?

I believe that we are only just scratching the surface of hundreds of eating-distress conditions in existence today. In a recent work-shop, many women admitted that they didn't know what 'normal' eating was (if there is such a thing). One young woman confessed that she never sits down for a meal. She exists on snacks that she eats on the run from one thing to another. She says, 'If I sit down to eat, I have to think about my food and what it may be doing to me. If I eat as I go, it's gone too quickly to notice – I don't have to confront it!'

Another lady said that she has lost touch with her own appetite cues. 'I just don't know when I'm hungry any more so I eat just in case I might be!'

A lovely and sensitive young man bravely shared his own feelings when he said that food to him meant shame. 'I was a big child with a healthy appetite which my parents tried to control. They were both extremely slim and were embarrassed by having a fat son. Eating, to me, became shameful and racked with guilt. I still can't eat normally and just sink inside when friends suggest going out for a meal!'

There are not enough names to classify all the ways in which people are becoming more alienated from food, themselves and their lives. The term eating disorder or distress doesn't even begin to describe the pain, disgust, distrust and guilt a sufferer feels.

We could make up fancy names for all of these varied and distressing eating conditions but ultimately they come under one heading which pervades and engulfs all others – body hurt.

As we continue to play mind games with our food, we reject the very thing which sustains our life force. When we eat with hate, we consume more hate. Every time we scream in horror and back away at the sight of a chocolate bar, we give away our power. Any time we allow food to fill us up with feelings of negativity instead of joy, we proclaim to the world how let down we feel as we refuse to let any goodness in.

What is happening to our society when we applaud weight loss more than the latest research for curing cancer, AIDS or some other life-threatening disease? What do we miss when we judge someone by their dress size and not their heart size? How can we accept that children as young as seven are being hospitalized suffering from anorexia?

We live in a world where a surgeon's knife can shape our hips and thighs but our minds are left weighed down by confusion, negativity and body-doubt.

It is ironic that women today are more visible, powerful, independent and liberated than ever before, and yet underneath the carefully constructed exterior there reigns body chaos and body hate – all wrapped up in a smothering blanket of body fear!

Naomi Wolf, author of *The Beauty Myth*, describes it perfectly (on page 10):

> Inside the majority of the West's controlled, attractive, successful working women, there is a secret "under life" poisoning our freedom: infused with notions of beauty, it is a dark vein of self-hatred, physical obsessions, terror of aging and dread of lost control.

Does my Bum Look Big in This Coffin?

Donna had her first inkling of anorexic behaviour at the age of 48 (although she had been anorexic for thirty years), after being admitted to hospital weighing just three stones! They told her she was dying and as they inserted the intravenous drip into her arm she felt a surge of fear as she thought, 'Oh my God, I'm never going to be able to fit into a coffin – I'm too fat!' She suddenly realized that she didn't want to die that day and although she had made previous suicide bids she just wasn't ready to die yet. As the doctors tried to prevent her body from shutting down she realized how sick she was as her only thought on her dying day was that her bum would look too big in her coffin! Up until that point Donna had denied her body battles and refused all help. Today, she still suffers from body hurt and fumes silently with body rage – but she's alive and she fights on. She **wants** to live and says quietly, 'The thing is I never realized how long it takes for a body to die – my heart packed up and my lungs collapsed and the decomposing process began and I was still alive. I realized then that my body was fighting for me and doing everything to keep me alive.'

Donna has a long way to go but she's determined to succeed. She says that she now realizes that not everyone is meant to be thin and if you try and fight to be something you're not then your whole life will be a struggle.

> I think like most women I look in the mirror and see things I don't particularly like.
>
> **Victoria Beckham (Posh Spice) Interviewed by Alan Corr in RTE Guide, 29/9–5/10 2001.**

Heal Your Fat

Fat appears to be at the top of the body hate and body hurt list. It seems that we will go to extraordinary lengths to evade and avoid being fat. Fat has become the part of a woman (or man) that is hated, jeered at, perceived as ugly, condemned, ridiculed, measured, weighed and not accepted in any shape or form. But fat is just fat – that's all it is and all it ever will be. It's the connotations and judgements that we put on to that fat that make our lives so hard and our bodies so full of pain.

Fat has become the ultimate scapegoat and distraction for not living our lives – just listen to some of the things we do to it:

★ We hate it with a vengeance
★ We starve ourselves to get rid of it
★ We have it surgically sucked out of us
★ We squeeze it into crushing corsets to hide it
★ We call it ugly, revolting, vile, hideous, disgusting

★ We deny it

★ We take pills to reduce it

★ We overexercise to burn it off

★ We loathe it as a part of ourselves

★ We spend a fortune trying to have it massaged,
  pummelled, bandaged or creamed away

★ We use it as a term of abuse . . . 'You fat so and so!'

★ We are ashamed of it

★ We talk about it endlessly

★ We grab handfuls of it and show it to our friends,
  proclaiming it as disgusting

★ We fear and dread becoming it

★ We blame it for not living our lives the way we want

★ We throw up food fearing that it will turn into fat as soon
  as we have swallowed it

★ We try to sweat it away

★ We put our bodies and health at risk every time we start
  some new diet fad that promises to rid our bodies of fat in
  2 weeks!

★ We feel that we are unlovable because of it

What we don't do is heal it, understand the message it brings, and respect it as a part of ourselves.

A dictionary definition of fat is: 'Fatted, well-fed, plump, corpulent, thick, substantial'. It does not say that fat is ugly, unlovable or revolting. Fat is not a moral indictment of who or what we should be – it is simply fat and it is the judgements we put on to fat that make it so dangerous.

What is even more extraordinary is that 76 per cent of women say that they feel too fat – **even when they're not.** It seems that we are not only afraid of real fat but of imaginary fat too. Uma Thurman, star of the movie *Pulp Fiction*, says, 'Since I've had my baby I've had body dysmorphic disorder. I see myself as fat.' If you have seen the film, you know how thin she is!

Body dysmorphic disorder is when the sufferer perceives themselves as fat, ugly or not right in one way or another – the sufferer may become hung up on just one part or feature of himself or herself, which they focus on repeatedly. Their lives may be ruined as they become more and more reclusive – afraid that the world will stare at their imagined deformities. I knew someone years ago who suffered from this condition. She believed that her skin was full of what she called 'pot holes' and would use bleach and a scouring pad on her face to try and 'smooth out the blemishes'. It was no use telling her that she looked great – in her mind she was convinced of her extreme ugliness. Unfortunately, like many other body-image-related disorders the sufferers could do great harm to themselves as they try to bring the pain they feel inside to the outside.

Stars – and Their Thighs!

> I wasn't going to stay on that fat regime forever . . . I'm ashamed to say the Brazilian-sized bum was mine – and I don't mean in reference to the people, I mean the country – I felt so big!'
> **Renée Zellweger, star of _Bridget Jones' Diary_ (size 12 max), in _Celebrity Looks_ magazine.**

What a shame that Renée Zellweger didn't share the same feelings as the sexy, confident and gorgeous character she played. This was the ultimate feel-good film as women everywhere warmed to the character of Bridget Jones as they identified with a woman who wasn't a size 6! For a brief moment that film gave us permission to believe that we could all be sexy, flirtatious and confident as we lived happily ever after in our 'big knickers'!

But, as in all movies it was just pure escapism and I for one was secretly disappointed when Renée stepped out from between the pages of a celebrity magazine looking literally half the woman she used to be. It seems so sad that the stars we love and admire for their talent, creativity and beauty don't love themselves and constantly feel under pressure to become even thinner, leaner and more body obsessed than ever before. It's not enough to be gorgeous in Hollywood – you have to be thin, under 30, conform to an impossible shape and have the 'perfect' face. In Hollywood, size 6 (UK 8) is deemed fat and everyone wants to be a size smaller!

Just think of the effect that this is having on the lives of today's celebrities and, more importantly, what effect is it having on ours? As celebrity bodies become tinier and more emaciated we have to ask ourselves where it will all stop. When size 4 is not enough and cosmetic procedures in the US recently rose to 5.7 million, what is our ultimate aspiration? Are we heading for a world populated by plastic pensioners – all over 80 but looking 35, living in bodies that are held together by botox, silicone, collagen and an unhealthy smattering of body hate? When young people look to the stars for a sense of their own identity and find only impossible ideals, hope is lost as body hurt begins to set in early. The Eating Disorders Association has recently noticed an increase in the number of teenagers calling the association's youth help line – identifying nearly 20 per cent of callers as being under 13. Whilst it is probably unfair to blame it all on the size of our shrinking stars and the media's obsession with thinness, it probably doesn't help matters and is a contributing factor.

High Street Surgery – the Ten Minute Facelift!

A leading beauty and pharmacy store has recently announced its plans for a walk in, walk out service providing botox injections for the passing public. Such is our acceptance and desire for all things plastic we can now have our wrinkles erased in our lunch hour! Botox is a derivative from the *botulinus* toxin and has the potential to be extremely hazardous as it is used to paralyse muscles. Botox can be injected into the forehead and, if not used in the right place or quantity, the results can be droopy eyelids or prolonged lack of facial expression. When it is used around the mouth similar symptoms may occur. This controversial move has prompted serious concerns by leading doctors who are worried that safety, practice and training may not be up to standard.

What worries me is that it has happened at all. Once again, this highlights how we are so ready to turn body hate into body hurt as we are prepared to put our faces under a needle in exchange for bland beauty. What's also interesting is that we don't even have to spend time on ourselves – it can all be squeezed into just ten minutes!

Cheat Death – Embalm Now!

What will be the next step? Do-it-yourself botox injections which will allow us literally to paralyse the parts of ourselves that we don't like? In the television comedy series *Absolutely Fabulous*, the characters Patsy and Edina inject themselves with the latest cosmetic product, Parallox! Needless to say they go over the top in trying to banish any sign of a wrinkle and end up looking like waxen zombies, not talking, not eating, not showing any emotion – not living!

Perhaps it is our denial of old age and death which keeps us seeking the eternal elixir of youth but, as with anything that promises you so much, there is a price to pay. Whenever happiness is dependent on the 'perfect' nose, a tiny bottom or a caved-in waist, then the price is too high.

Whenever we sculpt our bodies through hate or dislike we take a scalpel to our emotions too, reinforcing feelings of low self-esteem and negative body image. The truth is that no matter how thin or perfectly beautiful we may become, if we don't like who we are then we will never be good enough!

Bodysnippers

However, whilst we want to sculpt ourselves to our own design it seems that cosmetic surgery is here to stay. Two thirds of women polled in the *Top Santé* survey mentioned on page 123 would consider having plastic surgery, either now or in the future, if money were no object. The top five choices were liposuction, tummy tucks, eyes (reducing lines or redefining their shape), breast enlargements and face lifts. A television programme called *Body Snippers* points out that 'People really have the option for custom making their bodies.' It goes on to say 'We can cross the cultural barriers and sculpture a body to a different specification. If you're willing to pay – you can cross any racial boundary whether you crave a stereotypical black or Asian body or a thinner, less curvy European shape.'

'Dianne'

Dianne still walks with a slight stoop even though her tummy tuck operation was performed years ago. She looks out at me from eyes of anger as she tells me about her surgery. Dianne has always been beautiful and has worked hard to maintain the vision of beauty that everyone around her expects. She is married to an extremely wealthy man who is away for much of the time working and has three children who are also away at their respective public schools. Consequently, Dianne spends much of her time alone or at her exclusive health and fitness club. She recalled how even three workout classes a day did nothing to remove the stubborn layer of fat on her tummy which led her to seek surgery to flatten out and pin down what she described as her 'overhang'. Three days after her operation she was in agony and was corseted in a tight support bandage, which was wrapped around her middle. She was encouraged to get out of bed and try to walk around but as she did so she found that she couldn't straighten herself up and was in severe pain if she tried. The surgeon assured her that this would ease off and they allowed her home from hospital. Two months later she still could not stand up straight and went back to the surgeon who admitted that perhaps he had tucked the skin down a bit too tightly as there was no room for movement. Dianne was told that her skin would stretch gradually and that she would be able to stand up – eventually! Well, eventually she could – but her body still carries the memory of body hurt and body hate as it refuses to uncurl completely from its wounds.

> I'll read an article about somebody and they're extremely thin, and I'll say, see – I don't measure up!
> **Demi Moore in 'The Great Weight Debate' by Sarah Kennedy.**

Fuelling the Flames of Body Hurt

Of course, not all surgery goes wrong and many people are delighted with their results. However, any time you expose your body to any surgical procedure you put your body and health at risk. When you need a life-saving operation the choice to undergo surgery is clear as the benefits normally outweigh the risks. You accept the risk in return for life and health. Surgery itself is an amazing, wonderful gift which saves countless numbers of lives each day all over the world. Broken faces are reconstructed with the loving art and skill of a painter's brushstroke. However, when a healthy woman or man is driven to the knife as a result of body rage, any result that is not perfect has the potential to fuel the flames of body rage, leaving a fire inside forever smouldering with the glowing black ashes of body hurt – always ready to be re-ignited!

Does This Action Show my Body I Love it?

Whenever you are tempted to jump on the latest fitness band-wagon, follow the newest diet fad (because it promises two stones weight loss in two weeks) or banish your wrinkles through a state-of-the-art (but fairly toxic) new cosmetic procedure – just stop and ask yourself this question: 'Does this action show my body I love it?' Very often we say that we care for and respect our bodies but if our words are not backed up by our actions then what we say is empty and meaningless. A client once said to me as we spoke about his alcohol abuse that he wasn't an alcoholic. He said firmly, 'I respect my body! I can go without a drink.' I replied gently, 'Yes, but you don't – your body doesn't know that you're not an alcoholic – you have to show it!'

Every time we say that we care for or love who we are and then mistreat or neglect ourselves, we lie and perpetuate a deep mind, body and spiritual rift, causing intense inner conflict. Our actions give our thoughts wings and when those actions are congruent with our thoughts and feelings we can drop the body baggage and live in a body full of trust and confidence.

Body Harmony

There is a school of thought that believes that the body holds every feeling, experience, thought and action deep within its tissues. The body remembers everything we do, say or feel. We are our own living reflections of our lives, thoughts, feelings, dreams and experiences. Our bodies literally bear our pain and show where our hurt, joy, love and anger reside. Every time we hurt our bodies through body hate, the body knows, shudders and sucks the pain deep inside where we can't find it. It remains hidden away until maybe one day we put aside our ego's dominating voice of how we 'should' be and listen to our body's whispers of how we are. Don McFarland, in his book *Body Secrets* (page 37), puts it succinctly when he says this about the body:

> The body we exhibit today is completely of our own making. It's our history solidified in living flesh, a testimony to our dramas, and what may be even more ominous, a library of all our past adventures and misadventures on public display for all the world to witness.

Thus, whenever we ignore our bodies' call for love, respect, kindness and healing and treat ourselves badly or unkindly by word, thought or deed, our bodies know and store the pain. You may be able to lie to yourself about who you are but the truth is always present in your body's tissues and, as McFarland says, 'The tissues never lie to us. They don't know how.'

Every time you touch your body with dislike or hate, your body knows and the tissues contract and pull away. Every time you speak of your body unkindly or harshly, another part of you becomes stuck – more rigid. When you wound your body with words, thoughts, scalpels, food, drink or neglect, your body winces as the scars cut deep.

Likewise, any kind, loving action allows your body to open up and, like a flower, begin to blossom, displaying its true beauty to the world. A body knows when it is loved and responds to a touch that is compassionate, words that are aware and love that is unconditional. It's as if your body recognizes a friend and, like a cat on a warm summer's day, rolls over on its back, yawns and stretches out a long languid paw to welcome you in.

The Loved Body

The loved body is beautiful to behold and the world can't help but notice. People know that something has changed but they can't quite put their finger on it. Friends might comment that you seem happy today or that you look rested, peaceful, healthy or attractive. There's a glow – a radiance about you. Your skin looks fuller, rosier somehow, and you exude the subtle sensuality of a body that is loved. You might even appear taller and walk with a grace, confidence and ease that you have never experienced before.

Have you ever watched a child at play? They are so totally lost in the moment as they explore and delight in the world around them – all experienced in a body free from shame, doubt or dislike. Their movements are open and expansive as they embrace the world and their bodies reflect their feelings on a constant basis. They haven't yet learned how to hold their feelings in (along with their stomachs) and keep their bodies under strict, tight supervision, fearful that their bodies will tell the truth about them and expose their innermost fears, dreams and longings. As a friend once said, 'When I was 10, my body was a playground – I'm 36 now and it's more like a rubbish dump!'

Body Memories

Although we may forget the pain – emotional or physical – that we have been through, our bodies always remember and these memories may surface when you least expect them to.

Whilst writing this book I experienced a total loss in my own sense of body confidence as I collapsed and was rushed to hospital. As I lay on the floor waiting for the ambulance to come my mind was saying, 'Get up – don't be ridiculous – just get up!' My body didn't respond – I just lay there, shaking and feeling so bad. Logically I was trying to will my body into health while physically my body was doing what it had to do. I have never experienced feeling so split in two before except for the time I was going through my worst bulimic episode in my early twenties.

The hospital ran loads of tests which showed that physically I was fine but I still felt unwell. My abdomen hurt and although the ultrasound scan showed that everything was okay the doctors thought that maybe it could be an incisional hernia from a previous operation or a build-up of scar tissue. I thought back to when I was last in hospital. It was exactly this time three years ago and as I looked around me I went cold as I realized that I was in exactly the same ward in the same bed that I had been in before. As the surgeon examined me he asked about the old scar tissue and I told him it was from twenty odd years ago. As I spoke these words I felt an intense body quake as I remembered that this was the same time of year – almost exactly to the same date that I was in hospital all those years ago.

And then it really hit me. Prior to going into hospital at that time I had been mistreating and abusing my body in every way I could through laxatives, slimming pills, overexercising, drinking too much, smoking, lack of sleep, diuretic abuse and the vilest thoughts about me. A time when my bulimic behaviour was at its worst. My body was remembering all my most painful anniversaries and had taken me back to the time of my life that I had most hurt myself. The irony wasn't lost on me in that here I was writing a book on body confidence and love and was feeling just about as unconfident as you can feel as I struggled to find out what was wrong with me. I left hospital a week later – still shaky but with all tests passed with flying colours. I realized that I was remembering the time that I first lost touch with my body and began to neglect and mistreat my self. Perhaps writing the book had highlighted my own body awareness and triggered my body's memories – I don't know. What I do know is that as I lay there in the starched white hospital bed I felt a deep sadness well up inside of me and I cried and cried. At that moment I was aware of the deep love I have for my body and how much I had hurt it over the years and how it always came up trumps for me.

Heal the Body Hurt

Become aware of your own body memories – the subtle whispers that call you to stop, listen and take some time to heal the hurt.

Ask yourself these questions: 'When did I first lose touch with my body?' 'Do I remember a time when I began to neglect me in favour of something or somebody else?' Try to become aware of the ways in which you may have mistreated your body or tried to mould, coerce or force it to conform to an image you desired. Become aware of times when you feel particularly tired, or of a recurring pattern in any illnesses. Just allow these thoughts to sit with you – don't try to force an answer, there may be none at the moment. Just pose the questions and see what happens. Your answers may come in the form of images, dreams, feelings and thoughts, or even through your body itself. Even when we think that we have moved on and achieved a sense of body confidence, negative energy can remain deep within us, which may still need love and healing. I thought that I had released all my body demons years ago but clearly this was not the case as the writing of this book called for me to go deeper still. The cellulite on your thighs, the bump on your nose, the latest wrinkle, all need to be loved – not hurt and battered into shape or submission.

Move Your Body – Free Your Mind!

I wonder what your body would do right now if you let it. Would it sit taller, collapse in a heap, jump up and down, wiggle as you walk, slide onto the nearest bed or run naked along the beach delighted to have cast off its burdens?

Try it – go on just for fun – stand up right now and see what your body will do. Of course, you might just stand there doing nothing but that's good too – just be aware of how standing doing nothing feels. You can bet that even though you may be doing nothing, you will be feeling something – even if it's feeling foolish! Whatever you feel ask yourself if there was a time that you have felt this way before. The answers you come up with show you ways in which you can begin to explore and heal any body hurt you may have.

A client of mine found that she felt extremely silly as she just stood there and remembered a time when her mother had passed her in the hallway and found her just standing, day dreaming. She was clearly irritated with her being in her way and commented, 'Oh move out of the way, you silly great clumsy oaf!' She was amazed, as she had forgotten this incident completely and yet her body had brought it back to show her where there was still healing to be done.

> I've never liked myself and I have always had self-doubt so I thought that if I am as fit as I can be – and thin – then maybe I'll be good enough.
>
> **Geri Halliwell in *Celebrity Looks* magazine.**

Virtual Bodies

As we continue to project our innermost fears, insecurities and self-doubts onto our fat (real or imagined), we keep our bodies in a state of limbo – never sure if what we feel is okay and never confident enough to express our feelings through our bodies. It's as if we are always watching to see who's watching us and whether we look okay enough to be seen. We live our lives through virtual bodies – there's an experience there but we just can't feel it, which is summed up perfectly by the great line in *Star Trek*: 'It's life Jim, but not as we know it!'

But we need to know it! Our bodies are crying out to us to get down and get funky – they long to dance, play, jiggle and wiggle without censorship. Their very job description is to experience our lives fully and wholeheartedly, teaching us how to feel, love, cry, express and accept us as we are right now. Watch how the Hollywood film stars throw virtual kisses at each other – their lips never touch! Plug in to your computer and have virtual sex – the skin doesn't touch! Cry at how we live virtual lives – life doesn't touch!

None of us was born with a tag saying 'IMPERFECT'. In fact, if you put an apostrophe after the 'I' you get 'I'M PERFECT', and that's what we are. Perfect examples of ourselves!

Slay Your Body Demons With Love – Release the Binding Spell

Fat has become our fear in physical form and behind that fear lays anger, which we internalize back into ourselves, as we perceive our bodies to wear what we most hate. Hate then binds this to us. When you hate someone you are in effect binding and keeping that person with you forever. When you hate your fat or any other part of you, you keep your body hurt alive and all the closer to you.

Have you ever noticed how forgiving someone releases the hold that person may have had on you? The energy that kept you locked together has gone. When you release hate you allow yourself to become free from its seductive power and move on, breaking the spell that had you bound. Hate is a powerful force and its job is to keep you where you are. It hates change and, as an emotion, is stuck – its energy and vibrations are low, which in turn lowers and depresses your own state making you feel bad and dragging your confidence down with it! When you exchange hate for love, understanding or acceptance you begin to break the binding spell and set yourself free from your own imposed limitations.

You Cannot Have the Perfect Body – Only a Perfect Feeling About the Body you Have!

If you have tried hating and hurting your body into submission and are still left burning with body rage then your body and self may be starved of love. If your confidence is as low as your thoughts and if your feelings are as empty as the promises made by the next quick-fix diet, you may need to feed your body with love.

Love is the most powerfully liberating force you can feel and in the words of the song, 'lifts us up where we belong'. Ultimately, to love yourself 'warts and all' enables you to walk free from your body's chains and discard the body armour! Change happens from the inside out – from being **more** of who you are not less. If you want to change any part of you then do it with extreme love, gentleness and kindness by honouring the body you have. Ask your body how it feels before you impose the next strict diet on it – perhaps it may have other opinions on the foods it wants to eat. Perhaps your body knows better than the 'one diet fits all' mentality! Make sure that you and your body are both working on the same team and that it's not a dictatorship with you saying what goes and your body shrugging its shoulders and sighing, 'Okay, if you must'.

Swallowing Death

When body rage causes body hurt and this is expressed through an eating-distress condition such as bulimia or anorexia, the sufferer's body begins to break down as it becomes more and more starved of the love it so needs.

Let's get real – body hurt is dangerous and ultimately fatal. Our obsessions with the body beautiful can lead to the body battered. Eating disorders have one of the highest mortality rates of all psychiatric illness, with over 10 per cent of sufferers dying, either from the effects of starvation or through committing suicide. The effects of long-term bingeing and vomiting can cause ulcers, colitis, tooth decay, bleeding oesophagus, swollen glands, kidney and bladder infections, tremors, fainting, blurred vision, abdominal bloating, hair loss, menstrual irregularities, bags under the eyes, puffy face, weak muscles, rapid or irregular heartbeat, throat infections and brain shrinkage, to name but a few.

It seems so ludicrous that thousands upon thousands of people in the western world are literally dying to be thin whilst thousands more in third world countries are dying to live!

> We nourish our bodies with every impulse of trust and love, we poison them with distrust and hate.
> **Deepak Chopra in *Unconditional Life*, page 16.**

Stop the Silent Epidemic – Don't Spread the Dis-ease!

Think very carefully before commenting (either negatively or positively) about someone's size. You may be contributing to another's eating distress or adding to their sense of body discomfort and dis-ease. Every time we admire and praise weight loss or make negative comments about fatness we unconsciously stoke the fire of body rage. Whenever we refer to foods as being either 'good' or 'bad' we make it an issue. Criticizing ourselves only draws attention to the fact that we don't like what we see or perhaps who we are, which in turn reinforces a negative state of being for those around us. How often have you heard (or even said) that you have been 'good' or 'bad' today in reference to your eating behaviour? It's as if our days are summed up by the foods we eat and not by the life we live. When the scales dictate how we feel and success is measured by squeezing into a size 8 we cease to inhabit our bodies and begin to lose touch with our own innate wisdom.

Likewise, whenever you feel good because someone praises or comments positively on your own weight loss, be very aware that if a positive remark can lift you up, a negative one can bring you down! When your body image is dependent on positive feedback from others you are always at the mercy of a favourable word. Ultimately, our bodies are not up for comment, criticism or approval although in today's world it's as if our bodies are held up for judgement, found guilty and given a life sentence of body hurt and despair.

When you attack a woman's (or man's) body, you hurt the person and the very life they carry within their veins. You tug deep at their soul as they ask themselves why they aren't good enough and what they have to do to fit in! Every time we hate our bodies, we shatter our own sense of self-confidence, sending our self-esteem and self-worth plummeting.

We need to ask ourselves – what are we really angry at? Is it really our bodies or a society that equates thinness with perfection? The positive thing is that **we are that society** and just as we can be carriers of body rage and hurt we can also be the givers of body love and confidence!

Imagine this scenario: You are chatting amongst a group of women and one woman is desperately unhappy with her body. She grabs at her extra fat, points out her thin hair and moans about being too short. She wails that she hates herself like this. The other women don't join in with the body bitching and tell her instead that she needs to heal her body hurt and work with the parts of her that she rejects. They tell her that she is so much more than her hair, fat or height and ask her to see the warm, vibrant woman she is and get on with enjoying her life.

The woman stops crying, picks her chin up off the floor and begins to smile. No one has ever said this kind of thing to her before and she immediately begins to feel a little better and more confident about who she is.

Okay, perhaps this is a fantasy scene – but wouldn't it be great to see women swapping tips on positive body image and confidence instead of the latest 'Ten days to a tighter bum' diet sheet?

Body Shadows

I feel that it is the slight imperfections in all of us that make us unique and interesting. Sometimes it is our body shadows (our flaws) which make us beautiful – the quirky smile, the offbeat nose, the way our eyes crinkle up when we smile or narrow when we frown. The freckles we hate just make our skin more interesting and the mole we glare at every morning is really a beauty spot in disguise! The hips we try to squeeze into tight 'passion killer' girdles would dance their very own Jennifer Lopez-style tango if we would only let them!

But we don't let them – we reel them in and lock them down, too scared that once we start we may not be able to stop and our tottering tango may turn into a ravishing rumba! We need to live a little in bodies that are loved a lot!

We need to love the deepest darkest recesses of who we are as well as the sparkly bright bits we bring out on best occasions. Our body shadows make us beautiful and give us depth. Just as shadows add depth, form and interest to a painting, we too are made up of light and dark aspects – each balancing and completing the other and giving shape to the whole picture. Without our body shadows, we would be as flat and uninteresting as a one-dimensional character in a storybook.

There are days when I hate my body, like when I'm doing a runway show and everyone else is a toothpick and I feel like a moose!
Cindy Crawford in The Great Weight Debate by Sarah Kennedy.

Let Go and Live

Ultimately, we all have to learn to let go – of our looks, our youth, our athletic prowess, our loved ones, and eventually ourselves as we pass from this world into another. Our entire lives are a process of letting go, evolving and moving on. Our childhoods are left behind as we move into adolescence and from there, as young adults, we learn how to let go of studying and move into careers or jobs. Loss is a characteristic of our lives which, although it may be hard to experience at times, brings with it vast inner strength and understanding. We are not the same people we were seven years ago (even our bodies cells are different, having been broken down and rebuilt in an on-going process). We are not the same people we were this morning or even five minutes ago. Those moments have gone and we are somewhere new.

Perhaps our obsession with the body beautiful and remaining forever young is really a manifestation of our denial of old age, sickness and ultimately death. Is it our way of not being able to deal with the ultimate loss in our lives – ourselves? If we feel that we don't look 97, then we won't **be** 97 and perhaps the grim reaper will pass us by on his way collecting souls.

Accepting that we change, age, and one day will not exist in our physical bodies, allows you the freedom to live right now, instead of protecting and defending yourself against a tomorrow when you may not look, feel or be the same. When you accept that growing older is a natural part of your beauty and you love the changes you see, you become even more beautiful.

A friend once commented that the only time she felt she would ever achieve the ultimate thinness she wanted would probably be one week after her death.

It's a sobering thought that the only pieces of us that get to survive into eternity are the pieces of plastic and silicone we eventually leave behind. My mother remarked rather sadly as she had my father's ashes interred, that this was the smallest he had ever been. He had spent all of his short life battling with his weight and there was a dull sense of irony that he had finally achieved what he so wanted.

Loving who you are and where you are in your life gives you the freedom to feel eternally beautiful and confident. Whenever you find yourself comparing how you are today to how you were in the past, you allow unhappiness to darken your moments and take away the 'now'. Ultimately, 'now' is all we have and living in it creates its own profound beauty and confidence.

More Love Means More Confidence

The body journey is never over – there will always be new dreams, new challenges about how we think, feel and act towards ourselves and just when we think we've got it sussed our bodies will delight in new ways of showing us that there's more work to be done, more fun to be had and more confidence to feel!

7.
Body Love

Body Love is saying 'I DO' – to you.
Astrid Longhurst

. . . And as the hour of love arrived, she looked at her reflection in the candle-lit mirror by her gothic bed. Her dress – a deep crimson, open at the back – showed a flash of creamy white skin, just yearning to be kissed. Her hair was left naturally wild and free and her eyes smiled at the sensuality she saw in her face. Her rosebud lips delicately sipped the chilled champagne as she lay back against the sumptuous deep purple cushions on her bed – waiting with anticipation for her wintry lover.

Her heart beating faster now at the thought of their approaching night together, she pressed her expertly manicured fingers to her chest as her bosom heaved with longing and excitement.

Her entire body thudded with the deep drumming of her desire and as the fire burned brightly in the grate, the huge double oak doors opened and her silken lover strode towards the bed, taking her powerfully in his arms. Feeling her passion rise within her she pressed her melting body against his hard finely muscled frame as the cold night bound them even closer together.

She was breathless as her body betrayed the urgency she felt as they fell back against the crisp white sheets – their bodies entwined in their dance of writhing ecstasy. And at that moment she abandoned herself to him – giving all that she was as his fingers drank in every surrendering crevice of her skin.

> Hours passed and a ghostly milky sun stretched smoky tendrils of light into their sunken solitude. Her naked form lay adrift in his arms, careless and carefree – dreaming of spending an eternity with her soul beloved.

Cut to the screeching of brakes as reality screams to a halt right in front of us and we are awoken from our bodice-ripping fantasy.

How Was it For You?

When I was growing up I thought that only the beautiful people in this world were allowed to have sex, as that's all I ever saw on TV or in the magazines. I always wondered what everyone else did if they weren't beautiful or slim with endless legs and a tight flat tummy.

How could I ever compare to the uninhibited woman in the advert who snaked her lean, tanned legs around her partner's waist whilst he held her in a passionate embrace, lips pressed perfectly at the base of her throat as her head tilted back in total surrender? I could just imagine me trying out that pose – all hell would break loose as I visualized myself toppling over backwards, taking my partner with me as we ended up in an ungainly heap on the floor! How could I ever become like the wanton heroine in the romantic novels, ready to give her all in the throes of passion as she abandoned herself to the moment?

No, making love, as I mentioned earlier in the book, was a structured affair with every minute detail rehearsed and planned to the last degree. Nothing could be left to chance as I made sure the lights were dimmed, my night wear only revealed what I wanted it to reveal and there were plenty of sheets, extra cushions or cover-ups to hide any part of my body that happened to become partly exposed by a moment of sheer pleasure (God forbid!).

And in the morning I would make sure that I awoke looking as 'perfect' as the night before by getting up at six o'clock to brush my hair, wet my lips with gloss, dab some bronzing blusher onto my cheeks and splash a hint of perfume to cover the smell of fear. Fear that I would be found out, judged, criticized or left for someone who could make love without all the props of a well-organized film set around her!

And, when asked that time-honoured question, 'How was it for you?' I would murmur something incomprehensible into the sheets as I struggled to hide the fact that I didn't have a clue – I wasn't there! I had been far too busy directing and producing the scene ever to become involved in it! Looking back, I recall that there were some lovely moments when I allowed my body a fleeting glimpse of the pleasure I could experience before I caught a flash of my naked thigh and the stage manager in my head called out, 'Cut! Take 2!'

A Body Loved

A body that is loved radiates charisma and confidence. It glows with vitality and seeks to share its beauty rather than hide its perceived faults. I never loved my own body enough to share and indulge in the pleasure and joy it could bring me. I never felt safe enough to let go and become one with the moment – it was never okay for me to allow my partner to see me naked. For goodness sake, I didn't even see me naked! I kept my body firmly under the wraps of body shame, disgust and despair. The only thing that my body ever brought me was frustration. Frustration at myself – why couldn't I be like those fabulous images I pored over in all of the glossy magazines? Why did I need to eat when all the food did was make me fat? Why, oh why, couldn't I drip with sensuality as the film stars did – confidently and expertly seducing their men into undulating beds of unbridled pleasure? Why did I always feel like a child instead of a woman?

The answer to my endless search for body confidence and happiness lay in the fact that I did not love my body or accept it as mine. By refusing to accept my body, I ceased to live in it, rejecting my self and causing my mind, body and spirit to become disconnected and separate from each other. I felt alone in an alien world in which

I so desperately wanted to belong – to be accepted in a society full of what I imagined to be 'perfect' people!

In trying to fit in, I pushed my body even further away from my mind as I chose to live more and more in my thoughts of what an 'ideal' shape **should** be and how a sexy, confident woman **ought** to act. In fact, acting was what I did most of the time – I learned to put on a show and my outward, forced happiness hid the fact that I felt like a fake on the inside. The trouble was that every time I failed to live up to my own 'perfect' image of me my mind and body became more and more separate as what I fantasized about was not who I was. The result was a huge disappointment in myself and my inner conflict continued until there was a massive divide like a gaping chasm of denial that I could not cross.

The disconnectedness we feel when we reject any part of ourselves is mirrored through the rest of our lives – in our relationships, family life, work and play. When a body is unloved we are unable to fully give love, either to ourselves or to anyone else. We are also unable to totally receive love, as our body barriers are too rigid to allow any real emotion or sensation in. We have to wait until we are 'perfect' to be loved, to feel love or give love. Anything less than 'perfection' is not worthy. We are not worthy! Consequently our lives may be spent in waiting rooms – waiting for the right moment, the right time, the right look and the right body!

I realized that until I could give love to my body and subsequently to my self I would always be playing out my love-making scenes – on the surface I went through the motions but hidden in the subtext I remained deeply dissatisfied.

Boost Your Sex-Esteem

High self-esteem and high sex-esteem go together. When you feel confident, happy and at home in your body you are more willing to extend the love and happiness you feel towards another. Sexual confidence (like body confidence) is not about being able to per-form the most incredible stunts with your body – hanging from the chandelier by your big toe wearing only a smile is so 'yesterday' and has nothing to do with great sex or the most intimate love making! Fun, it may be (and incredibly impressive) but all the circus acts in the world won't turn you on unless you do first!

A survey in *Woman* magazine highlighted that 76 per cent of women feel that lack of body confidence affects their sex-life negatively, with 42 per cent preferring to undress with the lights off. Almost two thirds think that they would have better sex if they had an ideal body, and just listen to this:

> 91 per cent of women surveyed believe that women who are confident about their body have a wild sex life!

So, it's official – we know instinctively that feeling confident about our bodies and subsequently our selves leads to more pleasure – both in and out of the bedroom.

Unfortunately, sex, like body image, has become performance orientated, with everyone intent on achieving goals, doing it right, doing it well and doing it often. Just as we may suffer from low self-esteem our sex-esteem may be at rock bottom too!

It's not about intricate positions that tie you up in knots and cut off your circulation or about structured techniques or sex toys – although all of these things can certainly add to the playfulness and fun of sex. First and foremost it's about cherishing and loving yourself – feeling 'at home' in your body and knowing what you want. Sexual confidence is based on self-acceptance. It does not come from long legs, pert breasts or perfect cheekbones. High self-esteem and high sex-esteem are inseparable – knowing who you are and being confident in your body translates into high sexual confidence in the bedroom.

How can we ever fully abandon ourselves to the moment when we are desperately trying to cover our thighs, suck in our stomachs or keep our arms firmly by our sides so that our breasts don't slide underneath our armpits?

Having confidence in your body and love for who you are means owning your body, loving your individuality and revelling in your uniqueness. It also means being honest about what you want and sharing this honesty with your partner. Making love is a deep communication between two people. There are things said and shared with our bodies that are never voiced by our words. Maybe that's one reason why we keep our sexual expression firmly locked up in the tight grip of our negative body image, too afraid that our bodies will say something they shouldn't if we allowed them to feel free. Our bodies don't lie – they constantly show and reaffirm to us the state of our being.

Become Soul-Sexual!

Someone asked me once if men were the reason that women were so preoccupied with their shape, size and looks. Did women fight to conform to the ultimate sexual ideal to try to attract or keep men interested in them?

Personally, I think that this theory sells men short (as indeed it does women). In my experience it is very often the men who say how much they love their partners whilst the woman rages on against her body, picking out the faults in herself. Once again our views shape the way we refer and act towards ourselves. A well-built man will tend to see himself as strong and powerful, whereas a well-built woman views herself as weak and lacking in some way.

Initially, there may be some kind of sexual attraction or chemistry between two people which draws them together, but it's not as simple as big boobs, a tight, firm bum or a hunk with a six pack! Very often the most intense sexual feelings are triggered by the way someone moves or looks at you as if you are the only person in the world. Some of the most attractive people in the world are the ones who make you laugh!

A woman (or man) who is confident, happy and feels free within her body is attractive because she is turned on by her life. You **want** to be near people like this, as their energy and personal power lifts the energy of all those around them. Shape and size has nothing to do with it, neither does age, gender or ability. Something far more powerful than mere looks or appearance is occurring when two people meet, connect and fall in love. There is a soul link or bond as people are intuitively drawn towards those who yearn to share a part of each other's journey. We are far more than our bodies – we are soul sexual.

Have you ever fallen for someone who is typically not the type of person that you would usually go for? You don't know why but this person just attracts you in a way that you have never experienced before? Have you ever looked at someone and felt a deep intimate connection with him or her – a feeling that you must have met before as conversation flows easily between you both? This is your soul or spirit calling you to listen – to become soul sexual and connect on a deeper level.

If sexual attraction were as simple as two gorgeous people meeting up and hitting it off because they were both so stunning then all the couples on the TV programme *Blind Date* would pair off on each and every date. Cilla Black (the presenter) would spend a fortune in hats and the programme would lose its appeal. Half the fun is watching the most unlikely-looking couples get together and fall wildly and passionately in love!

Body Karma

The word 'karma' derives from the Sanskrit word meaning 'action' and refers to the law of cause and effect – that every action we take leads to a future action in a never-ending sequence of events throughout eternity. Buddhists believe that we create our own karma through every word, deed and thought and that it is this internal state of being which has tremendous impact on where and how we are in our lives today.

In other words, everything that you have ever felt towards yourself and every action (or non-action) has brought you to this point in time and has helped create the person you are today. Equally, if you wish to know what results will appear in the future for you, just look at the causes or actions that you are setting in motion now.

In terms of body love and confidence the way we feel about our bodies and how we treat ourselves has come about as a direct result of our past actions, thoughts and beliefs. If we feel in a negative or unloved state it is because our past actions have caused this. Our beliefs have shaped the way we feel about our bodies and, more importantly, ourselves.

Ultimately, the concept of karma teaches us that we alone are responsible for our lives and the way we feel – good, bad or indifferent! Everything that we suffer and all that we enjoy is the result of our actions.

It's a powerful concept and one that can have a profound effect on your own personal chain of destiny.

'Body karma' is the term I have used to highlight the link between our body beliefs and actions and how loved, confident and alive we can choose to feel. Body karma calls you to **own** your body and accept the way you feel about you. It asks you to believe that the uplifting, energizing and loving thoughts and actions you give your body today will create a loved, happy and supremely confident body of tomorrow.

Body karma is about getting in touch with your body – the more in touch you are with your body, the more you know who you are and what you feel. When you can touch yourself with love and tenderness you can also extend your love and spirit to another human being – touching them with your love. The more you can smile at your imperfections and love them as a part of you the more you can look at another's flaws and accept them as something which goes to create their own uniqueness.

Colour Your Life Beautiful

Loving your body is more than a vague sense of 'I'm all right' – it reaches outwards into every single area of your life, heightening your senses and calling you to see the magic in your universe.

Loving your body is cherishing who you are and prizing your life. When you see your body through eyes of love and wonder you also see your life in a new and brighter way. Everything comes into focus as you notice the world around you. Suddenly you find beauty all around and even the dullest day becomes infused with a deep splendour that previously you didn't notice. It's as if you have stepped through the looking glass of your soul into a land where everything is sensuous, magical and full of rapture.

When you behold your body with love, you colour your life with beauty and nothing is ever the same again. The rain feels sensuous and erotic on your skin, you turn your cheeks to the sun so that they may be kissed warmly and the light breeze buffs your skin with pride.

As you see your body with compassion, understanding and a deep gratitude, your life also takes on a new meaning as it comes alive in full technicolour – bright, shiny, gorgeous and packed full of special effects! The mundane becomes marvellous and even the smallest thing you do becomes an act of love.

The reverse is also true. Have you ever noticed that feeling low, negative or depressed causes your world to collapse in a cloud of doom and gloom? It could be the most spectacular summer's day outside but you hardly notice as your thoughts are turned inwards with feelings of futility, despair and frustration about you. Your inadequacies become the central point of your life around which everything else revolves. Opportunities and moments of pleasure and fun are missed as your world becomes bound up by your body barricades.

I lost the first part of my life to the body blues and began to colour the rest of my life black. Nothing excited me, called me or drew me – and as I turned away from myself, I shunted my life into a little corner where I could keep a critical and accusing eye on it. Like a naughty and wayward child, I kept punishing my body until it could only come out and be visible again if it was good and behaved properly!

'Buns' at Daybreak!

I cannot overemphasize the difference that loving your body and becoming more of who you are can make to your entire life and existence here on this planet. I wish that I could take your hands in mine and show you a world swept up in the throes of body love. I would love you to feel the heartbeat of the universe dancing through your veins as your life pulsates to your very own disco, funk, soul or classical beat! Wouldn't it be great to look our wrinkles in the eye and laugh in the face of sagging skin? We could throw caution to the wind as we confronted our 'buns' at daybreak and shot them with a love potion! Our love for our bodies knows no bounds; our spirits will soar on clouds of uplifting thoughts. And it's not over until the fat lady sings . . . only she doesn't think of herself as fat any more – so we fly onwards forever!

Become a Free Size at any Size

Loving your body means becoming free of the chains that bind and hold you down. It means becoming involved with you as a person and getting excited about your life. You love yourself unconditionally and wholeheartedly because you are here and this is who you are.

You realize that you don't have to try to fit in any more because you are confident of your divine place in this world. You know that you belong. It's a fantastic feeling as you are no longer caught up with the latest 'look', diet, beauty or fitness fad. You set your own style at your own pace and pick and choose what you will or won't do. And, whatever you decide to do is done through a deep love, care and respect for who you are.

Body Love is Body Work

Body confidence and love don't just happen. They require work, courage and a deep commitment to you. Every day is a choice about how you are going to feel, whether your thoughts will be uplifting or restricting and how you will respond to certain life situations. Loving you means loving your life and living authentically – being who **you** are and not a carbon copy of someone else. You cannot love someone else unless you know how to love yourself first. Trusting another person is impossible if you have no trust in yourself. Being comfortable and happy in another's company won't happen unless you can learn to be happy and relaxed in your own. This is why body confidence and loving who we are is so vital in our lives because without a loving relationship with ourselves we cannot hope to achieve a loving relationship with anyone else.

Someone I knew years ago spent her life in search of the perfect partner. She was a successful businesswoman in her own right and had worked hard to create all the good things she enjoyed in her life. She was creative, enterprising and independent, yet something was wrong – she said that she only ever felt like half a person. In relationships she gave her all and possibly too much as she demanded that her men complete the picture for her – to make her whole. She had always felt that in order to love herself, she needed to be loved and valued by her partner first.

Unfortunately, this was a tall order for many of the men she dated as they struggled to keep up with the constant reassurances she craved – telling her that she was lovely, beautiful, sexy and intelligent on a daily basis! Time after time her relationships would end, making her feel even more incomplete as every failed partnership highlighted her insecurities. The final straw came when she became pregnant by a man she thought was her soul mate. On announcing her pregnancy to him (dreaming of the perfect family, a country cottage and the token climbing rose round the front door), he legged it as fast as his feet could carry him!

Feeling absolutely devastated she eventually sought out the help of a counsellor who quietly allowed her the space in which she could begin her own body (and self) work. Years later, she's a single mum but feels content within herself and no longer seeks completion by another. She says, 'I like myself now and when I look in the mirror I'm happy with my lines – they show I've used my face and not been afraid to show my emotions. Anger, laughter, pain – they're all there. When I look at my face I see my life.'

She told me that she always felt that she was never a valid or worthwhile person in her own right and that she now realizes that the missing 'something' was the lack of love and belief in herself. Her own experiences have had a huge impact on how she is bringing up her daughter. She tells me, 'Every day I tell her that she's beautiful and loved – not so that she becomes arrogant or cocky about her looks but so that she believes in who she is. I would hate her to grow up half a person like I did. She already has confidence in herself and an awareness that I spent my whole life searching for.'

I agree with her – let's show the children of this world that it's okay for them to be who they are. No, it's more than okay – it's absolutely essential! Along with regular subjects such as geography and history, let's include body confidence on the school curriculum. Let's teach our children to have pride in who they are so that they don't spend a lifetime apologizing for themselves. Let's create a world in which we bring out their talent instead of their fear and harness their power instead of fostering weakness and dependence on something as transitory as beauty. In doing this, we might learn to love ourselves a little on the way, as it is said that we teach what we most need to learn.

It's never too late to begin again – never too late to become what we always imagined we might be. Make each and every moment an expression of your love, respect and trust in your self and let's teach the children of this world by our own inspiring examples.

Live the Sensual Life

Begin to work on this loving relationship with you by getting back in touch with your body, feelings, fantasies and desires. Start to live a life full of sensuality. Turn your days into on-going moments of delight and the most ordinary chores into experiences of awareness and pleasure. From this moment on, concentrate on living your life in the 'now', being fully aware and switched on to what you are doing, thinking or feeling. For example, the next time you wash up the dishes really focus on what you are doing. Feel the heat of the water on your hands and the way the soapsuds pop and froth between your fingers. Be exactly where you are and focus **only** on washing up – not on what you are going to do tomorrow or later that day or on how you still have so many things to get done. The only thing you have to do is wash up so wash up the best you can and give it your full attention. Watch and feel how sensual washing up can become.

Any everyday activity can become a sensual experience. The next time you walk upstairs, tune in 100 per cent to how your body feels as you carry yourself upwards. Be aware of your hand on the banister and of how hard or light your grip is. Notice the way your weight shifts as you take each step and whether you tread lightly or heavily. How does your breathing change with the effort of climbing and do you walk fast or slow?

When you make the bed, really feel the softness of the duvet or sheets as you smooth them out. Delve into the lightness of the pillows and become aware of the texture and weight of any blankets or throws. Make your bed with total awareness and do it the best you can, really giving it your full concentration!

Does this all sound mad? It does a bit I suppose, but it works! Try it! No one needs to know what you're doing – only you know that what once seemed like a boring job has now been transformed into a bite-size munch of sensuality! Let your life turn you on as you connect more and more into everything that you do and how that makes you feel. Stop tuning out of your reality and turn on to yourself.

Body Bliss!

Extend these daily tasks into your body care routines and make the next shower or bath you take the most blissful, sensual experience ever! Instead of just roughly or quickly washing your hair, really massage your fingers deep into your scalp, noticing if there are any points of tension. Feel the water cascading over your body and watch the patterns it makes on your skin. Really smell the shower gel or shampoo and notice how your skin glows from the warmth. It's great fun and gives washing your hair a whole new meaning! Now, when someone tells you that they can't go out as they are too busy washing their hair, you'll know exactly what they are up to – living the sensual life!

When rubbing in body lotion or moisturizer, turn it into a sensual experience by touching your skin with love and care. Really feel your skin underneath your hands as you smooth in the cream. Affirm in your mind that you care for and love your body. Talk to your body and become totally aware of the area that is being touched. Try not to avoid certain parts or places that you may usually ignore. Show your body that you are now nurturing and loving you and make this the best shower or bath of your life (well, until the next one). Become fully involved in the whole experience.

Every time you manage to do this, you make a deep mind, body and spirit connection. There is a sense of coming together and working as one as your entire focus is on loving you.

However, it's not always the easiest thing to do. Many people find that they cannot bring themselves to touch their bodies with love as they are so used to denying and punishing that part of themselves. Ask yourself if there are parts of your body that you avoid looking at or pampering. I always used to avoid massaging body lotion into my stomach area, as it was the part that I wanted to hide from. I didn't accept it as a part of me and consequently it became neglected and uncared for. One of my hardest body love lessons was to integrate my stomach back into my body and begin to love it unconditionally. However, the day I managed to do this was brilliant. I had decided to apply fake tan to my body as I knew there was no hope of a summer that year and was happily massaging this wonderful bronzing lotion into my arms, neck, shoulders, hips, legs and feet. It was a tinted lotion so I could see immediately any areas that I had missed, so it was with some amusement that as I looked in the mirror my stomach shone out like a great white moon against a golden desert! It was so clearly obvious that I neglected my stomach in favour of other, more acceptable areas! As my stomach turned a glowing shade of brown under my hesitant fingers I looked again in the mirror and realized that I looked complete. My stomach finally joined in with the rest of my body and I felt a sense of resolution and wholeness that I had not experienced before. Seeing the sensuality in your life calls you to see the sensuality in yourself – it also keeps you fully centred in each moment of your life.

More! More! More!

It can be hard work staying in the 'now' as we are constantly pulled away by distractions, daydreams and the drama of our lives. However, the more you are able to check in with yourself and become aware of how you are feeling at any given moment, the more body love you will generate. The next time that you feel out of balance or pulled in conflicting directions, just put yourself right back in the moment. Focus all your attention onto where you are, what it is you are doing, how you are feeling, what you are thinking, and what your intuition is hinting at. Be 100 per cent where you are and connect to the 'now'. It is amazing how clear your life becomes when you choose to live in the present rather than flee to tomorrow or skulk around in the cobwebby corners of yesterday. By harnessing your focus in this way you give yourself more choice as you are aware of how you truly feel. You opt to go with **your** flow and not **the** flow, and know that you'd do anything for an interesting life and not merely an easy one!

The more you wear clothes that you love and that make you feel sensuous, the more you eat foods which give you real pleasure and health, the more you urge yourself to be more of who you are, the more powerfully confident you will become. Look at the word that is constantly cropping up here – MORE! Every time you become more of who you really are you take a step closer to your own fabulous authenticity – the real McCoy. Anything that leaves you feeling less is suspect – whatever it may be. If you're on a diet that's stripping the pounds away along with your energy and health, then that leaves you with less. Less weight certainly, but also less health, vitality and long-term energy. Being thin and ill does not promote body love or confidence in you. It sacrifices one thing in favour of another and perpetuates the mind, body and emotional rift even further as you betray your body's health for thinness.

I went to my doctor for a mini medical check up the other week. It's a great service as it gives your body its very own MOT as blood pressure, cholesterol, etc are checked. As I was chatting to the nurse she told me about one patient who had lost a lot of weight on a new diet and how delighted she was with it. However, when her cholesterol was checked it showed that it was raised quite significantly from her last test. Feeling rather concerned by this the nurse pointed out that perhaps she would be advised to ease off on the diet, to which her client replied that she would rather be thin and have high cholesterol!

Body love and confidence are not about gaining one benefit at the expense of another – there's no need and it's pointless if you end up superslim but suffering from heart disease!

All Time is Your Time!

Have you ever thought about the real meaning of the term 'quality time'? I have always thought it strange, as all of our time is quality time. People are going to work earlier, doing things faster, investing in time-saving gadgets so that they can spend 'quality time' with their families, friends or loved ones. Unfortunately, very often that quality time becomes stressed time! Such is the pressure for that 'quality time' to be 'perfect' that it usually turns out to be nothing like we planned and may end up in rows, disagreements or just a vague feeling that something is wrong. It also suggests once more that we put our lives on hold as the only moments that are valid are given the label 'quality', suggesting that all that has gone before is somewhat insignificant or unimportant. Make every single moment of your life 'quality time'. You don't have to wait for that perfect moment or stress yourself out by reorganizing your entire daily routine. It's simple – just love the things you do, when you do them, and do them with all of your attention, awareness and focus.

Even the things that you don't enjoy doing become a new focus of awareness when you do them as well as you can and notice how you are feeling in the moment.

In doing this, you stay centred in the 'now' – in your life as it happens – moment by moment. You don't wait for those elusive three hours when you expect everything to fall into place as if by magic! You live your life as it is – right now. You also stay connected with and aware of your body, emotions and thoughts.

This is another powerful key to body confidence as it asks you to engage with your life on all levels. Body love is more than feeling great about your hips – it is about feeling amazing and amazed by your entire life and all that you do. A body which is loved, loves life!

The effects of living confidently in a loved body are far reaching as you realize that your life is important – every single second of it. In becoming aware of each moment as it unfolds you also become aware of your choices – whether to feel great and interested in what you are doing, or not really bothered.

It's so easy to slip into neutral and just plod along every day in the same old way – thinking the same thoughts, doing the same things in the same old way. Have you ever been driving to a destination and, when you arrived, realized that you didn't actually remember driving there? How many of your days are spent really being fully present in your life and fully in touch with your body?

This is it – it isn't a dress rehearsal and we don't get the chance to replay that scene again. So often we squander the moments we could be feeling beautiful and loved by just not being there at all! Can you recall how you felt this morning or even five minutes ago? Don't let your life pass you by unnoticed – **don't let your body die unloved!**

Become present – become visible and involved in your life, your body and your dreams. Make everything you do an act of love – from taking the dog out to putting your make-up on!

And the next time you don't wear your favourite clothes or use that fabulous dinner service because you're saving them for best – stop and remember – this **is** best! This is it!

Smiling From the Inside Out

It can be difficult to stay living in the 'now' and our focus is all too easily distracted away from ourselves as we fall into complacency, routine and security. However, each time you manage to live and love the moment you're in you glimpse a sparkle of eternity and become one with the universe. There's an inner smile that starts with your heart, chuckles with your spirit and laughs out loud with delight every time a moment becomes truly lived. Every time you notice that the leaves on the trees are turning gold as autumn blows in, or see something new in your partner's face or notice how the sun makes even the dullest building bright – every time you really see the depth and beauty of your life you create an inner smile. An inner smile becomes a beacon of radiance and light which shines out its brilliance from within you!

I remember the day I realized that I felt such contentment about my life and who I was. I was pottering about in the kitchen and the day was one of those blustery 'can't make up its mind' kind of days. As I went from one thing to another, tidying up and clearing out cupboards, I realized that I was smiling. Not about anything in particular – just smiling because I was happy, because I was 'me'. There was no big 'nag' going on in my mind and there was a wonderful feeling of calm within my body. For the first time I wasn't racked with guilt about what I had eaten or hadn't eaten, how much exercise I had done or that there were one hundred and fifty chores that I still had to do! I had decided the chores could wait – my life couldn't!

From that day on I have been subject to frequent attacks of smiling and when I catch myself in the middle of one of them it makes me smile even more. Body love and confidence seems to be the cause of this contagious experience and happiness is the very welcome symptom!

September 11 – The Day That Shook World Confidence

We all have our own personal memories of that tragic, dreadful day when terror struck straight into our hearts, as our confidence crashed along with the World Trade Center's twin towers in New York. The horror of that day continues long after the smouldering fires have gone and thousands of people have been lost and mourned, their lives cut short by hatred.

The impact of that day lingers within our very souls as we question our own safety here in this world. If the unthinkable can happen in a busy city on a bright September morning it begs the question – are any of us truly safe anywhere?

A client summed up her feelings to me when she said, 'It just puts it all into perspective for me. I've spent my whole life feeling unconfident and full of hatred for my body, yet when I saw those poor people trapped in the buildings with no hope for escape I thanked the Lord that I was still here. My own body issues paled into insignificance as I realized that I was one of the lucky ones – I still had my life! It seemed somehow sacrilegious to moan about my heavy legs or bad skin when there were people who would give anything to have lived another day – regardless!' The people who died that day didn't get another chance to enjoy their lives and many spent their final seconds desperately trying to phone their families to tell them that they loved them one last time. In the last moments of our lives it is not the size of our hips or the shape of our bodies that we are concerned with. Our last moments are about love, peace and being able to let go.

If this has taught us anything, it is that we all so desperately need to learn to love ourselves and heal the wounds of our past. Perhaps if we can accept, love and respect who we are, then we can also accept, love and respect others. When we can look at another human being and love them for their differences and prize their uniqueness then we rock our entire world with love rather than shattering it with hate.

The Alarm Clock That Woke the World

When our very confidence in the world has been shattered, there is only one place left to go – within us. Having an inner confidence and trust makes your body a safe place to live, no matter what is going on outside. The events of that day put us all on notice to live our lives fully and with as much love, happiness, compassion and confidence as we can muster. Our sense of safety and security will never be found in the latest look, the biggest car, the sleekest legs or a massive bank account. The tragedy that occurred on that fateful day didn't care who it took – rich, poor, gorgeous, young or old – it just took.

By making your body a safe and loving place to be, you are always 'home'. And when all around you shakes with fear you know that you are strong enough to cope with whatever changes may be ahead.

September 11 once again highlighted to me how precious this gift of life is and how we need to extend our love into every part of it. When you love your self – mind, body and spirit – that love exceeds far beyond our physical form. When we love and value others we seek to uplift rather than to destroy, and our entire energy vibrations are raised – helping to heal the planet.

What a Difference a Day Makes

When you realize that your life can change in an instant and that nothing stays the same, you begin to live your life consciously with a heightened awareness. Every moment becomes potentially magical. Every experience can illuminate a new thought, action or pathway for you to explore. Even your sadness is lived fully without you trying to push it away – you know that you are safe to feel this pain and that this too will pass. Your life becomes a series of choices and you know that you can change how you feel by changing your thoughts and beliefs. There is a sense of incredible freedom, as you know that nothing is written in stone – everything changes, including you. Your thoughts of yesterday do not have to become your beliefs of today, and the enriching, uplifting thoughts of today will powerdrive you towards a fantastic tomorrow.

Don't be fooled – change doesn't have to be a hard slog and a constant struggle. Change can happen in an instant and our entire lives can be changed in a day. It all comes down to what you choose to think, how you desire to feel and the actions you take. Loving your body is literally only a thought away and you never know – the body you've always dreamed of may be the body you've always had. You've just never noticed it before!

Part Two

The Body Journey

A guided adventure into the
world of Body Confidence

An Interactive Workbook Experience

Introduction to the Body Journey

The body journey is a mythological interactive adventure. It is a cross between Indiana Jones, Buffy the Vampire Slayer and Harry Potter!

You are the hero – the star!

As you step in and out of the story, you are asked to complete certain tasks (in the form of exercises), which help build body confidence, self-esteem and body love.

The story itself is an entire guided visualization and can be read in its own right without the exercises. (You may wish to record the story onto a tape and listen to it as a powerful meditation/visualization on its own.)

However, any of the images found in the journey can be used as meditations, symbols or visual affirmations. Just conjure up the picture in your mind and play out the scene.

Work through the journey in order. Each chapter takes you to a new destination, where you will be asked to choose, create, imagine and build a new picture of how you see yourself. A dynamic, energetic, vibrant and powerfully confident you!

All of the exercises work on the 'power of three' (the mind, body and spirit connection) to leave you feeling refreshed, balanced and energized.

Have a fantastic journey!

1.

Your Story

The Decision

From the moment we are born we are on a journey. We each have a different and unique path to follow. No two journeys are the same – no two lives are the same. Each journey teaches us more about the person we are and may yet become. I believe that we each choose the type of journey that will teach us what we most need to learn. Some of us find that money issues are the way we learn best and our lives are plagued with situations involving money. Some of us experience lives which deal with illness and recovery, others' lives are full of challenges involving relationships.

Many choose the body journey as the ultimate way of understanding their strengths, weaknesses and own unique power to love the person they are.

I chose the body journey. I chose it wholeheartedly and went for the full experience! No short cuts, no easy way out, I opted for the entire trip – good, bad and indifferent! My body journey began the day I was born and will continue up until the day I die. It doesn't stop – it just becomes more exciting! I understand how every moment of change has been centred on my body and that my body is and has been my greatest teacher. It's a humbling thought that the thing I hated and hurt most in my life did the most to teach me how to love and accept me.

This life is a gift – your body is the most valuable possession you will ever own; something to treasure, look after and allow to shine in its own full splendour! The problem with this gift is that many of us don't know how precious it is because somewhere along the way it became tarnished or lost. The shine faded until there was only a tiny glimmer of a sparkle left and even that was hard to see.

We undervalue this gift thinking it's eternal and will go on forever, but it won't – some day this tiny jewel will cease to exist in these surroundings and its chance to be really seen, loved and appreciated will be gone. Some day our chance to shine, love and enjoy our bodies and our lives will be gone.

From this moment on it is up to you to write your own body story. There is no right or wrong way to do this – it's all about how you feel, what you want and how you travel through the body journey workbook. The body journey is a step-by-step process which takes you on a mythological journey, designed to stimulate your senses and imagination by powerful image-work. The fairy story format provokes archetypal images as you wander through lands once forgotten and reawakens the magical child within. You will meet gremlins and ogres, helpers and heroes, but you are the star! As each part of the journey unfolds you will discover parts of yourself which may have become lost, hidden or just forgotten about over the years. None of us know what amazing precious gems we are hiding until we begin to look for them and realize that they were there all the time – we just couldn't see them!

Very often the most precious are the ones you have to dig deep for – they won't come out easily but when they do the light they give out is awe-inspiring. Every one of us has the ability to shine out our own unique, special light in our own way. What a vision that would be, to see the world lit up by people!

This part of the book, 'The Body Journey' was created from my own personal experiences and inspired by the many people I have worked with over the years who have shared with me a little of their own journeys. Each one of us has found our own way to end the body wars and make peace with a body that has become our best friend and companion through life.

Wish You Were Here?

The journey takes you through some wonderful and long-forgotten places. You will create your own body magic as you find the keys to open the locked doors of body/self love. You can choose to go fast or slow – there is no rush, no competition. The time you take is up to you. Try to travel through the 'destinations' in order as each one takes you to a new starting point – each one is a healing process in its own right.

Allow yourself to really create and write your own body story – make this book your own. If you feel so inspired, write, doodle or make notes in the margins. Cut out and stick in pictures or sayings that inspire, motivate or move you to laughter or tears. Highlight words or sentences that have a particular meaning for you. Make this book lived in – jump inside it and make it your home. Invite your imagination to play and allow yourself to star in the leading role. Anything goes – try not to censor your thoughts or feelings, make this a place where you can explore, relax, fantasize and dream. Remember, it's your story and your journey.

It's the Most Fun you Can Have Between the Sheets!

Having body confidence is about having fun and the journey is also about creating fun, excitement, laughter and passion in your body and life. All of the techniques, exercises, stories and games are written to inspire, motivate, excite, create and entice you into designing your own world. A world where you know how to love and support you, you care and value who you are and you have a great time along the way!

Create Your Own Body Confidence Kit – Tools for Change

Over the next few pages you are going to design, create and put into action your own body confidence kit. Few travellers begin a journey without an idea of where they are going or the things that they might need to help them on their way. This journey is no exception and by the end of this chapter you will have created your own body magic pack.

It will contain your body vision of how you want to feel, a new body blueprint (words to love your body by), and your own siren song of change, your personal creed and body values. With this pack you can go anywhere feeling confident as new challenges present themselves in your life. It provides the very basis and foundation of feeling great about you and gives you a solid structure upon which you can build, increasing self-esteem, self-worth and a loving body image. Have fun!

The Journey Begins

The Pledge

Every journey begins with a decision to travel – a choice to move from where you are now to a place you have yet to discover. Every new journey brings new destinations, new ideas and, with that, a willingness to change. This journey is different from any other you may have experienced as it asks you to travel to the places within yourself which you may have forgotten about, or left unvisited for many years.

This body journey begins with a commitment or a pledge to yourself that you are ready to take a step towards feeling confident and happy in a body that you cherish. It is a way of saying to yourself that you are **worth** doing this for and that you value who you are.

Remember, your words have immense power and when you sign the pledge you are affirming to yourself that you are ready to change. The change may take days, months or years but by signing your name you are giving your mind instructions to begin the process of body love and confidence.

My pledge

I (Insert your name) _____ am ready to change. From this moment on I am willing to see myself in a kinder, more loving way. I am open to exploring my thoughts, feelings, dreams and fears in a non-judgemental way. I am ready to giggle, sing my own song, write my own words and caress my thoughts. I am now making a positive choice to love my body, respect myself and enjoy being me – shining my own unique light out to the universe. I understand that this will take work, commitment, honesty and acceptance from me and I am prepared to begin my body journey with an open mind and trusting heart.

Once I have signed this pledge I understand that the journey has already begun, as my word to myself is the most powerful law in the universe.

Signed
_____
Dated

Where am I Going?

As in any journey, one of the first things you need to decide is where you are going.

I love poring over holiday brochures just drinking in the photographs of those deep-blue skies, endless white beaches and majestic swaying palm trees. I can almost imagine that I'm there already and in a way I am. As I gaze at the photographs my mind begins to fill in the missing pieces. I can almost feel the heat of the sun on my skin and the warm breeze playing with my hair. I imagine myself relaxing, reading books, dining out in candlelit restaurants, swimming with dolphins, watching the golden arc of the sun setting, and seeing my body turn a gentle healthy shade of brown. As I imagine all of this, it is as if I am giving my mind a mental blueprint to follow. An instruction of how I want it to be. Remember, the subconscious mind cannot tell the difference between reality and fantasy. On one level I am actually there in my imagination; I almost don't need to go as my body starts to produce physical responses to my imagined thoughts. My pulse rate lowers, my breathing deepens and there is a deep sense of well-being and contentment.

Over the next few pages you are going to create an entire picture of where you want to be and how you want to feel about your self and your body. You are now setting in place a new code of instructions for your mind to follow and act upon. Just as you can produce physiological responses to an imagined scene in your mind, you will now begin to walk your talk with confidence, and think thoughts which are helpful and not harmful. You will begin to express your respect for you in all that you say, do and believe.

Journey's End

So, where would you like to be? How do you want to feel? In terms of the body journey you need to begin by knowing where you want to end up. You have to have a destination in mind – where are you travelling? Many people have half-hearted thoughts that they just want to feel a bit better or a bit more confident about themselves. I ask them, 'What does better mean? How does better feel? What does better look like? Describe better to me!' If you don't really know what you mean by feeling better or what confidence means to you then your journey may become very confused. The first thing to do as you begin to write your own body story is to know the ending first. Most authors will map out the characters of their book in minute detail and work out the plot – they have a good idea of the ending before they start at the beginning. Knowing where you want to be gives you the route to follow – the steps to take. In building a house the architect will sketch out a design of what that house will look like. The builders don't just go in and say, 'Right boys, lets see what happens with this one!'

Imagine setting out on a journey, not having a clue about where you will end up. Whilst it might be quite good fun to wander your way through different places, exploring and changing your mind as you go, it could also be deeply frustrating.

I met an old school friend the other day who I hadn't seen for about twenty years and we decided to go for a cup of coffee and catch up on our lives. We began to reminisce about our school days and she said that she wasn't where she thought she would be at this stage in her life. I wondered where she wanted to have been, to which she replied that she really didn't know. She looked a bit wistful as she said quietly, 'Just not where I am'.

Very often, we are not specific enough about what we want from our lives or how we desire to feel and we find ourselves in a place which is unfamiliar and miles away from where we would truly like to be. When we feel that our bodies are in that place, there is a sense of our lives being out of balance. We cannot run away from ourselves as our bodies are our homes. We need to know how we want to feel, and love and look after the skin we're in!

To change something externally, we need to have it happen first in the internal world. In other words, in order to feel confident, safe and secure in a body we love and appreciate we must create it first within our minds and in our thoughts.

Feeling Good About Yourself is Not an Accident

There are some days when we wake up and just feel that everything is right with our world – it's an inner feeling of happiness and contentment that fills mind, body and spirit. Most days, however, we have to work at making ourselves feel better. Our bodies will always seek to maintain optimum health and well-being and our thoughts determine our actions. Everything we ever do is preceded by a thought, so our days and how we live them are decided by how we think about them.

Many people feel that life is something that is thrown at them, whether they like it or not, and they either catch it or miss it completely! There is a pervading feeling that they are powerless to exert any control or direction over it. We may not be able to control events and situations around us but we do have the power to take charge of the way we respond to that event. Feeling great about your body and who you are means that you take full responsibility for your thoughts, actions and feelings on a daily basis. You know that feeling good about your body and your life is a choice. You can either choose thoughts that bring you down and make you feel that you lack something in some way, or you can choose thoughts that bring you joy, compassion, kindness, love and respect. Whatever it is that you wish to attain – be it happiness, success, health, inner calmness or beauty – you must first programme the results into your mind. If you don't have your own plan of how you want to feel, think, act and live then someone else has the power to make you fit into their plan – their ideas of how you should feel, think, act and live.

Body Mapping

The first part of the body journey and creating your tool kit is for you to map out the way you want to feel about your body. It's about programming your mind to believe that this is how you now desire to be. In essence, it's about letting go of the old thoughts you have about your body and coming up with new and more empowering ones to describe yourself. Remember it is not important that you may not believe these words to be true about you. It's about choice – about choosing a new way of thinking. It calls you to create a new way of believing, feeling, thinking and appreciating your body. You may have had years upon years of limiting and unkind thoughts about you and your body but from this moment on your point of power lies in the present. You are now actively choosing to change that old CD and listen to new, more harmonious sounds.

Your Body Blueprint – Words to be Loved by

The words you use to describe your body are important to how you feel and treat your body. If the words that you have used up until now have been negative, unkind, or just downright rude about yourself then here's where you begin the reprogramming.

Choose at least three words from the following page to describe your body in a more positive, kind and uplifting way. For example, I used to think that my stomach was revolting and would always comment that instead of having a six pack I had a party pack! That was one of the nicer things I said about myself – most often my words were harsh, unloving, unforgiving and full of hate.

I now choose to describe my stomach as . . . smooth, lovable and softly rounded. Just applying those words to that area of my body makes me feel more compassionate, sensual and loving towards myself.

Have a look at the Body Wishes list and choose your own way to describe your body, adding any other words you may think of which are not on the list. Be creative and imaginative – you are recreating your body image and opening the doors to feeling great about you. You may use the same word twice or more often if you wish.

Body Wishes

Impressive ★ Supported ★ Active ★ Adorable ★ Beautiful ★
Vibrant ★ Wonderful ★ Powerful ★ Welcoming ★
Delicate ★ Aromatic ★ Lovable ★ Graceful ★ Unique ★
Capable ★ Sexy ★ Inviting ★ Firm ★ Divine ★ Supple ★
Smooth ★ Full ★ Strong ★ Enchanting ★ Dynamic ★
Amazonian ★ Delightful ★ Attractive ★ Athletic ★ Bubbly ★
Delicious ★ Free ★ Rounded ★ Sensual ★ Dainty ★ Erotic ★
Grand ★ Fantastic ★ Bouncy ★ Exquisite ★ Comfortable ★
Shapely ★ Defined ★ Full of life ★ Charismatic ★ Healthy ★
Efficient ★ Awesome ★ Breathtaking ★ Sweet ★ Dramatic ★
Gentle ★ Long ★ Fit ★ Radiant ★ Superb ★ Charming ★
Bright ★ Glamorous ★ Ace ★ Brilliant ★ Refined ★
Willowy ★ Embracing ★ Glowing ★ Fine ★ Soft ★ Finely
muscled ★ Cool ★ Cheeky ★ Appealing ★ Amazing ★
Sleek ★ Lovely ★ Gorgeous ★ Heroic ★ Glossy ★
Fabulous ★ Captivating ★ Feminine ★ Passionate ★ Cute ★
Flowing ★ Juicy ★ Great ★ Aquiline ★ Classy ★ Stunning ★
Lived in ★ Dazzling ★ Creamy ★ Tantalizing ★ Blooming ★
Tight ★ Energetic ★ Exotic ★ Flexible ★ Open ★ Impish ★
Bold ★ Sensitive ★ Stylish ★ Uplifting ★ Warm ★
Seductive ★ Happy ★ Kissable ★ Relaxed ★ Loving ★
Supportive ★ Beautifully formed ★ Lithe ★ Scrumptious ★
Tasty ★ Calm ★ Romantic ★ Expressive ★ Earthy ★ Shiny ★
Satisfying ★ Valued ★ Cared for ★ Special ★ Magical ★
Okay ★ Deep ★ Translucent ★ Rosy ★ Silky ★ Touchable

My body is _____ _____ _____

My hair is _____ _____ _____

My eyes are _____ _____ _____

My skin is _____ _____ _____

My nose is _____ _____ _____

My mouth is _____ _____ _____

My ears are _____ _____ _____

My face is _____ _____ _____

My neck is _____ _____ _____

My shoulders are _____ _____ _____

My breasts are _____ _____ _____

My arms are _____ _____ _____

My hands are _____ _____ _____

My ribcage area is _____ _____ _____

My stomach is _____ _____ _____

My genitals are _____ _____ _____

My hips are _____ _____ _____

The tops of my thighs are _____ _____ _____

My inner thighs are _____ _____ _____

My outer thighs are _____ _____ _____

My knees are _____ _____ _____

My calves are _____ _____ _____

My ankles are _____ _____ _____

My feet are _____ _____ _____

My bum is _____ _____ _____

The backs of my thighs are _____ _____ _____

My back is _____ _____ _____

My waist is _____ _____ _____

Isn't it amazing that, when there are so many beautiful and enriching words we could use to describe our bodies and our selves, we usually choose only a handful of really rather unpleasant and unhelpful ones!

Before you continue just be aware of which areas of your body were the easiest to create new words for and which you found most difficult (if any). Notice your points of resistance and write them in here.

The area I found the easiest was _____

The area I found the most difficult was _____

The area which you found most difficult highlights the part which may need your extra special love, kindness and attention as you go through the journey. These are also the areas which may teach you the most about how to love you and express your confidence.

Now, fill in the following sentence – choosing just three words to describe the way you now choose to see yourself. Choose any of the words you have already used or come up with three new ones. Select words which hold the most power for you or those that seem to leap out from the page and into your mind!

I choose from this moment on to see myself as

_____ , _____ and _____ .

This is now your own magical affirmation about who you are.

Repeat it often by saying to yourself, I am

_____ , _____ and _____ .

Get Diana Ross or Ally McBeal to Help You!

In future, whenever you feel tempted to talk about yourself or your body in a disparaging or unkind way, replace the old words with the new ones you have chosen to describe you instead. Make yourself pause, stop or take a break as soon as you are aware of the old thoughts tapping at your mind, trying to get in. Gently acknowledge they are there and then immediately change them to the new thoughts you have decided upon.

A friend told me her technique for doing just this. Whenever she thinks something nasty or unkind about herself she imagines Diana Ross suddenly appearing singing, 'Stop . . . in the name of love!' She says that it literally makes her stop and think about what she is about to do. I loved this, as it was just so appropriate and amusing.

It reminds me of the TV series *Ally McBeal* in which the men in the office enlist the help of Barry White to make them feel sexy, attractive, confident and desirable. As they look in the mirror they imagine they hear the sexy bass beat kick in and as the music builds, their bodies begin to groove to the throaty words of, 'You're my first, my last, my everything!' You can see their confidence and sex appeal increasing as they stand taller, puff out their smartly-suited chests, raise an eyebrow and adopt a look that says, 'Am I a god or what?' Brilliant stuff!

In one episode they 'lost' Barry – they just couldn't get him to appear in their minds and subsequently couldn't get a good feeling about themselves. They drooped around the office, their tails between their legs, whimpering that they were useless and unattractive and that no woman wanted them! (If you know anyone like this, offer him or her a bit of Barry White and see if it does the trick!)

Choose Your Song

The above examples make me laugh and appeal to my sense of the ridiculous. I have several songs that tend to come up at different times. When I am feeling timid about my thoughts or what I have to say, I play an old Helen Reddy number in my head, which goes, 'I am woman, hear me roar . . .' That always makes me feel powerful and I picture myself as a proud lioness, standing high on a mountain, shaking my golden mane and roaring out my song to those around me!

When I'm feeling unconfident my mind sings to me, 'I am who I am – and who I am needs no excuses.'

One of my clients chose another Diana Ross song to help her

stop feeling unworthy and unconfident. She gently reminds herself that, 'It's my turn – to be what I can be – this time it's for me.'

Jenny, a bright, vivacious lady, shouted out in a workshop that her theme tune would now be Frank Sinatra's classic *I Did it my Way*, and another lady joined in saying that she would choose the rather newer Anastacia number, *Paid my Dues*! She added meaningfully, 'Because, boy, have I paid them!'

Another woman got up and asked if hers could be It's *Raining men*! I say if it works for her and makes her smile, feel good or changes a low state of being to one which lifts her spirits – then go for it!

What's **your** song – **your** theme tune? Who could you imagine coming in to save the day, lift your spirits or make you feel loved? Allow your thoughts to play with this one or write down the first ideas that come into your head. You can have as many songs as you need – just make sure that the songs are positive, inspiring, and make you happy!

My songs are:

_____

_____

_____

So far in your journey you have signed a pledge honouring your self and your word, programmed in a new body image blueprint and selected songs to help you break any negative, unfulfilling ways of thinking.

If you Loved Your Body . . .

In order to create the full picture of what body love and confidence mean to you and make sure that where you are going is where you desire to be, you must now move into exploring the confident you. Remember, we are starting this journey at the end – giving your mind, body and spirit clear and specific instructions of your chosen destination – of what you want.

Imagine that you really loved your body and your self – so much so that you always strive to nurture your feelings, cherish your soul and give yourself the best that you can.

In this next section you will be asked what you would do and how you would live if you loved your body and your self. Let your imagination and dreams flow. There are no limitations – fantasize, create and allow your loved body to tell you what it needs.

Try and go with the first thoughts or images that come into your mind. This is your story, your fantasy, and your own creation.

When you love someone you want to do the best for that person. You seek to bring out that person's best qualities – encourage them to live their dreams and express themselves as an individual. You try to give them foods which will nourish and sustain them and make sure they are rested and happy.

Imagine this person is you and fill in the blanks. Do not let the fact that maybe you would not wear jeans right now or would never go swimming because of how you feel about your body restrict your thinking. If you want to wear jeans, a mini skirt or thigh-high boots and go parasailing in a thong, then do it here – in your imagination!

1   If you loved your body (and self) what kind of clothes would you enjoy wearing?

_____

2   If you loved your body (and self) what foods would you eat?

_____

3   If you loved your body (and self) what exercise would you do?

_____

4   If you loved your body (and self) how much sleep would you make sure you got every night?

_____

5 If you loved your body (and self) what type of pampering treats would you give it?

_____

6 If you loved your body (and self) how would you relax?

_____

7 If you loved your body (and self) what would you tell it?

_____

8 If your body (and self) could be any emotion what would you want that emotion to be?

_____

9 If you could be any sound in the world what would that sound be?

_____

Your Personal Creed

Now, take the answers from the previous questions and write them below to create your own personal creed, adapting them to make it flow.

I (write your name here) _____ love my body and myself. I express this in all that I say, do, believe, think and feel. Everything about me says something of the way I value and think of myself.

The way I dress expresses my own unique sense of style and I particularly love to wear (1) _____

I take care of me and eat the following foods, which nourish me and give me pleasure **(2)** _____

My body stays fit, strong and supple by **(3)** _____

I always make sure I get **(4)** _____ hours sleep per night.

I pamper myself by **(5)** _____

and make sure that I relax by **(6)** _____

I keep my mind, body and spirit focused by telling myself that **(7)** _____

In my heart I feel **(8)** _____

I hear my spirit calling to me in the sound it loves so dearly – the sound of **(9)** _____

I am safe and I am home in a body I trust, value and care about.

Read back your personal creed and refer to it daily or copy it and put it up somewhere in the house where you will notice it. Or, if you prefer, keep it in your handbag so that you can have it with you at all times.

What do I Value Enough to Take With Me?

So far in the body journey you have built up a picture of how you desire to see yourself and how you want to feel. The next step is to become clear about what it is you value highly enough to take with you on your journey. What are the things about your body and yourself that are most meaningful to you? Values are important – they give meaning and purpose to life and in this exercise, you will be taking a look at the values that you hold most dear.

The values listed below focus on the physical body, emotions and your inner qualities. Other types of values such as financial security, a new car, work, etc are not listed here as, although they certainly help to build a picture of what you want, they are more external values and we are working firstly on our inner selves.

How important is it that you possess (or work towards the development of) the following values? Rate each one on a scale of 1 to 5, with 1 being 'not important' and 5 being 'extremely important'. (Add to the list any other values that are important to you.)*

1 Athletic ability
2 Good health
3 Strength
4 Good eyesight
5 Manual dexterity
6 Good hearing
7 Self-esteem
8 Flexibility and suppleness
9 A satisfying sexual relationship
10 Intelligence
11 A positive attitude
12 A strong immune system
13 A good digestive system
14 Spiritual growth
15 The ability to heal quickly
16 Good circulation
17 Gentleness
18 Compassion
19 Stamina
20 A sense of humour
21 Curiosity
22 Contentment
23 Sensitivity
24 Understanding
25 Happiness
26 Effort
27 Sincerity

* Adapted from *Create Your Own Reality* by Nancy Ashley

28 Acceptance	**35** Personal freedom
29 Truth	**36** Religious faith
30 Forgiveness	**37** Solitude
31 Self-respect	**38** Passion
32 Energy	**39** Self-expression
33 Open-mindedness	**40** Loyalty
34 Intuitiveness	

The next step is to list all the values you rated 5 and then to rank these in order of importance, with the most important value at the top and the least important at the bottom. You may find this difficult to do as you have rated **all** of these values as 'very important'. However, through forcing yourself to make a choice from among your most important values, you will find out a great deal about what really matters to you.

The values I listed as extremely important (5) are:

These values in order of importance are:

You may be surprised by what you list as the most important of all your values, and by others which come lower down the list.

This exercise proved very enlightening for one client when she found that she had put 'self-esteem' at the top of her list but 'self-respect' came at the bottom. She puzzled over how these two very similar qualities (both extremely important to her) could be so far apart when she evaluated them. After a few moments of silence she came up with her own answer as she said, 'I guess that I probably do have quite a high self-esteem. The way I think about myself is usually positive – I mean I do think that I'm intelligent and creative and good at what I do – but I don't respect myself.' I asked her if she could expand on this, to which she replied, 'I don't really respect myself by the way that I treat myself. I let myself get overtired, work too many hours, eat crap food and drink too much. I think of myself highly but treat myself badly and that's how I show myself that I don't truly respect me.'

In this one exercise she had highlighted the main area where her body and self-confidence were low. The way she thought about herself was not being translated into the way she looked after herself and as such there was a huge discrepancy between her thoughts and her actions. When you have this kind of inner conflict between what you think, feel and do, your body, mind and spirit become fragmented. It's as if each is talking another language and there is no translator to get the message across. You might say that you love your body and think highly of yourself but when these words are not followed by actions which support them then there is a great deal of confusion and distrust within.

It's as if someone is telling you constantly that they love and think the world of you but then they ignore and treat you carelessly. You don't know what to believe – they say they love you and yet their actions speak otherwise. Imagine what would happen if we brought a child up by telling them one minute we loved them and smacking them the next minute. They wouldn't know what to believe and how to trust that anything you said was true.

Total body love and confidence are about every different part of you backing the others up so that you literally walk your talk, live your dreams, speak your own truth and express your needs.

Finally, having put your values in order of importance, go down the list, take each value in turn and ask yourself the following question:

How do I show these values to myself?

For instance, if you said that 'good health' was your most important value then take a moment to think how you create (or don't create) a good state of health. If 'happiness' was on your list ask yourself how you make yourself happy. Go through your entire list until you know how you manifest your most important values in your life.

My most important values (in order) are:	I show these values to myself by:
1	
2	
3	
4	
5	
6	
7	
8	
9	
10	

(*Fill in more as applicable*)

Take a moment, as you complete the first part of your journey, to thank yourself for spending the time doing the exercises, thinking about you and knowing that you are worth every single piece of energy you put into this book – by reading it, creating it and living, loving and doing it!

> . . . *All around you falls a hushed silence as far off in a land you've only ever dreamed about – 'the Land of Body Love and Confidence' – someone is softly calling your name . . .*

* Adapted from *Create Your Own Reality* by Nancy Ashley

2.
Ticket to Ride

Copy and keep

The Body Journey Experience
AFFIRMATION CARD

Name _____

One-way ticket to body love and confidence.

Valid for as long as it takes   *Non-transferable*

Sign your name and put your 'ticket' in your purse or bag – keep it with you at all times. This is your own affirmation card – your ticket to ride. Look at it often and remind yourself of your commitment to you and the journey you are on.

The affirmation card is a symbol and key to your own unique sense of body confidence. It also heralds the fact that you are already in the process of change. On a subconscious level you have now given a directive to your conscious mind of how you desire to feel, think and act towards your body and the confidence you wish to generate.

This part of the journey is connected to change and your support system, and is about taking stock of where you have been and where you want to go.

The Journey Unfolds

Imagine walking out on the most beautiful summer's day. Experience the feel of the ground beneath your feet, the warm sun on your skin and the breeze softly whispering through your hair. Your eyes take in the beauty of the scenery around you and your spirits lift, as you smell the sweet honeysuckled air. There is excitement and anticipation as you leave your past behind and venture into today. You smile, as you know that this is your moment — your time — when the magic of you will come into being and you can come home to a body you love, respect and enjoy with a passion you have never felt before.

The Body Toll

As you continue on your journey with your ticket firmly in your hand you notice that ahead of you is a huge sign, which reads 'TOLL GATE — YOU MUST PAY THE BODY TOLL!' A huge ogre — the like of which has only ever been seen in fairy stories — guards this gate and as you draw closer he demands that payment must be made before you can pass. You realize that you don't have any money but the ogre growls contemptuously that the toll is not paid by money but by your suffering over your body! He demands to know what feeling bad, unconfident or negative has cost you during your life and asks you to write down the price you've already paid by feeling bad about your body.

He wants to know what disliking your body (or any part of your body) has cost you emotionally, physically, spiritually, mentally and financially.

Think back over the years and try to identify how not liking your body or your lack of body confidence has impacted on your life. What has it cost you? What are the things (no matter how small) that you would have loved to do but didn't because of the way you felt about your body? How much money, time or energy have you spent on your body? What has it cost you on an emotional level and has it affected your health in any way? Take a few moments to think about these questions and then write your answers below:

The cost to me (for not loving my body) has been:

Emotionally _____

Physically _____

Spiritually _____

Mentally _____

Financially _____

As a gift to you for your honesty the ogre softens and smiles a big toothless grin as he tells you that you can have anything you want in return for what you have paid.

Write down what it is you desire now that you have body love and confidence. In essence, what will body confidence give you? What are all the things you would love to do if you felt happy and confident enough in you and your body? How do you want to feel? How would you like to be? Is there anything you have put on hold but would love to do, experience or have as part of your life? Whatever it is, list it below.

Emotionally _____

Physically _____

Spiritually _____

Mentally _____

Financially _____

You thank him and he waves a great shaggy claw at you as you pass through the toll gate.

You walk down what looks like a yellow brick road until you notice a massive flat screen television lodged right in the centre. On it is written in neon blue:

Who wants to feel like a millionaire?

Before you realize it, you shout out 'I DO!' at the top of your voice. At that moment the screen changes and the smiling amiable face of the TV presenter beckons you to come closer. As you look into his animated face he tells you that in order for you to complete the journey and feel like a millionaire you need to have a strong support structure in place. He tells you that both winning a million and feeling like a million require great inner strength as both have the power to change your life completely. As in any journey, you need to know and have in place people, strategies and options that you can turn to if you feel lost, confused or just in need of some positive reinforcement. As you nod in agreement he tells you that you have three lifelines to help you on your way and these are — phone a friend, ask the audience and go fifty-fifty!

He asks you to put your support structure into place and write down your ideas in response to the following questions:

Phone a Friend

Who can you call to give you love, support, a hug or back up if you should need it? Identify one or more friends who will be there for you if you find yourself feeling unconfident or unsure. It's up to you whether you tell them that you are working on dramatically boosting your body confidence. Just knowing they are there sometimes is all the support you need.

> **My phone a friend(s) is (are):**
>
> _____

Ask the Audience

The 'audience' here refers to support groups, hobbies, activities or events that you can involve yourself in. It is about supporting your actions as you make your journey in a way which connects you to others who can share your interests. In my early days of transforming my own body image I joined an eating disorders group and creative art class, as these were two ways I found that I could share and express my feelings within a safe and supportive environment. There are many options you could choose – for instance, joining an aqua-aerobics class, learning a new language or skill, or taking up a new sport – golf, badminton, tennis, bowling, etc – joining a poetry reading group, drama club, choir or going to see live bands if your interest is music. You could also become involved in local community events, committees or charities. Whatever is closest to your heart – do it!

> **The hobbies/groups/projects I would select to provide another support for me are:**
>
> _____

Go Fifty-Fifty!

Going fifty-fifty is about weighing up your options and keeping your choices firmly in your mind. Whenever you feel doubtful or uncertain that you can change, go back to the list of what feeling negative has cost you and what feeling confident will give you (the body toll). Choose the most important reason for travelling this path. Write down here what it is you would most love to feel, think or be able to do. What will you gain most in your life from feeling good about you? What is it you really, **really** want?

> **Having body love and confidence will give me:**
>
> _____

As you complete writing out and devising your support system, you feel a warm breeze tangle your hair playfully and then a stronger wind nudging at your back, pushing you forwards. As you allow your body to be carried onwards you realize that you are now in the loving hands of the winds of change and there is a feeling of excitement as your journey unfolds before you. Everything and anything is possible and you smile at your own possibilities.

The Winds of Change

Faster and faster, the winds of change urge you on, calling out to you in their soft ghostly echoes — tantalizing you with thoughts of how beautiful and wonderful you could feel. As you reach out your arms to embrace your destiny you realize that you are suddenly in the middle of a huge circle, which is surrounded by high walls made of soft, seductive padding. There are cushions everywhere of all different shapes, sizes, fabrics and colours and enough food, drink, books, videos, music and all kinds of amusements and distractions to keep you occupied for the rest of your life. It looks a lovely place to stay but you notice that there is no way out — no door, exit sign or even a window! As you search for some kind of gap in the circle a huge booming voice resounds around you, saying, 'This is the Comfort Zone — there is no way out except through the winds of change!' You look around to find where the voice is coming from but see no one, so you call out into the space around you, 'I am on a journey — a journey to find body love and confidence and all that this brings. Tell me how I may leave the Comfort Zone!' The sound of laughter fills the air as the voice replies, 'Most people never leave the Comfort Zone — it is my job to keep you exactly where you are even if you don't like it.' You feel a rush of indignation as you shout back, 'Why?' There is more laughter as the voice continues, 'Because I hate change — it's scary, different and frightening! My job is to keep you safe — keep you doing the things you've always done, thinking the thoughts you've always had and staying exactly where you've always been. Stay with me and I promise you safety, security and no surprises!'

Gently, you shake your head and say, 'I know that you've tried to keep me safe and for that I thank you, but I've come this far — I'm on a quest in search of me and I need to leave my Comfort Zone.' All of a sudden a piece of paper materializes in your hands saying:

'To leave the Comfort Zone you need to interrupt your patterns, break your routine and see your world with new eyes! Every day for the next 21 days you are invited to try to incorporate these small changes into your life. No one need know that you are doing them — only you. Good luck!'

Twenty-One Days to Body Awareness

For the next 21 days take a step out of a negative or low body image rut and allow yourself to increase your body and self-awareness. These various tasks are designed to help break patterns and interrupt routines, highlighting your own awareness. Have some fun as you notice which exercises make you feel uncomfortable, outrageous, awkward, silly, amused, frustrated, anxious, tearful, loved or empowered. Don't judge or criticize your self and if there are any tasks you don't want to do – don't! Everyone has their own time in which they choose to do things – you know what is right for you. If you choose not to do any of them just be aware of how you feel about not doing it and whether that throws up any interesting connections, feelings or answers for you.

Day 1   Smile as soon as you wake up – make it the first thing you do this morning.

Day 2   Eliminate the word 'but' from your conversation all day!

Day 3   Do not put the TV, radio or any other distractions on in the morning as you get up.

Day 4   Go into a kids' toyshop and buy yourself something you don't need, that has no use but makes you laugh, smile or is just totally ridiculous!

Day 5   Open all doors with your non-dominant hand all day today!

Day 6 Buy a fake tattoo and place it anywhere on your body.

Day 7 Look in the mirror and gaze deeply into your own eyes.

Day 8 Buy yourself your favourite food and eat it on your own, without any other distractions – no TV, no family or friends, no children, no nothing – just you and your favourite food!

Day 9 Do not comment on anyone's appearance at all today.

Day 10 When you go to bed tonight, rehearse in your mind how confident, happy and energized you are going to feel tomorrow.

Day 11 Be aware of your posture all through today. Sit tall with your chin lifted and shoulders eased back and down.

Day 12 Make no comments, judgements or criticisms about **your own** appearance today.

Day 13 When you go out today pause, take three deep breaths and really notice your surroundings.

Day 14 Buy a newspaper or magazine that you would never usually buy, and read it.

Day 15 Take five minutes – don't do anything. Don't talk or move – just be!

Day 16 Wear your watch on your other wrist – be aware of how habits take a little time to change.

Day 17 Say something positive about yourself three times today. Slip it into conversation – make sure you highlight your strengths.

Day 18 Make a date with you! At a designated time, go to a private place, for instance your bedroom or bathroom (somewhere you won't be interrupted), and blow yourself a kiss in the mirror.

Day 19 Find a piece of music that you really, really love and play it – loud!

Day 20 Light a candle as a symbol of your own inner light and beauty.

Day 21 Applaud yourself for being who you are right now!

Destination – All Change

Change is something that we are all doing, every minute of every day from our conception to our death. Our bodies are changing all the time – old cells are being broken down and new cells are being built up – a continual process of renewal of which we are unaware. However, for many people, change is a fearful process and something to be avoided at all costs. People stay in jobs they dislike, relationships that hurt, places they feel stifled in, and around people who pull them down. WHY? Because it's safe! They may not like where they are but it's what they know.

Having confidence in your body and self asks you to change . . . and the journey challenges you to take a step into the unknown and create a new place for you to be.

Be aware that as soon as you start to change in any way your comfort zone may act up, as it perceives its old familiar ways to be under threat. You may find yourself listening to a voice within that tries to stop you from what you are doing by telling you it's silly or not worth the effort. Be also aware that any change you make may have a knock-on effect on those who are closest to you. As you change, you also are challenging those around you to look at themselves and how the 'new' you impacts upon their lives. They may have a vested interest in keeping you the same and any changes may make them feel insecure, uncertain or fearful. It's not bad – it's just what change does and the way to break the comfort zone's clingy embrace is to treat it as if it were a very small child. As soon as you are aware of any feelings of doubt, fear or nagging that it's all a waste of time, you can be sure that the comfort zone is up to its old tricks. As soon as you hear these murmurings, talk to your comfort zone in a calm reassuring way, explaining that you hear its advice and that you are grateful for its love and protection BUT you are still going to go ahead with what you have decided to do.

A Body Worth Changing For!

One of the comfort zone's favourite lines is 'Why bother?' It persuades us that nothing will ever change anyway and all our hard work will be for nothing.

As long as we are alive there is still time to change, grow and experience a new way of thinking, feeling and being. You need persistence, focus and the ability to walk steadily but surely towards your goals.

The Gremlin on Your Shoulder!

I always imagined that my comfort zone was, in fact, a furry, wizened little gremlin who sat curled up on my shoulder and for the most part was asleep as long as I continued to do the same things in the same old ways, getting the same old results I always got. As soon as I deviated from my allotted path, the gremlin would open one sleepy eye, peer around widely and mutter a small, 'Uh oh! What's going on here?' The best way to comfort and reassure him was for me to imagine that I was stroking his little tufty head and telling him in a soothing calm voice that everything was just right and that there was no need to worry or be concerned. Gradually, instead of giving me a hard time he would close his eyes, snuggle in closer and whisper into my ear, 'I guess you know what you're doing – call me if you need me.'

Soothing Talk

Whenever you feel uncomfortable, unsure or are aware of your own gremlin sitting on your shoulder nagging you, try soothing yourself with words that are calming, reassuring and loving. Love your comfort zone for trying to protect you, and use its energy and power to help you get passionate about what you want. Talking to your comfort zone is not a one-off event – you may find that you need to reassure yourself at frequent intervals during the day. Remember that every single bit of energy you put into working on yourself and healing your body hurt is worth it because YOU ARE WORTH IT!

As you look around, you notice that a door has appeared and as you walk through it an old wizard who looks remarkably like Gandalf in The Lord of the Rings *meets you. His eyes are the most beautiful deep violet you have ever seen and, as you gaze in wonder at the beauty and strength of the lines in his face, he holds out his hand to you and beckons you to come closer. You know that you are in the presence of immense power and as you take his hand you feel a deep connection to your spirit. He smiles gently as you tell him that you feel you know him and ask him if you have met before. He rubs his silver gossamer beard thoughtfully as he tells you that he is 'time eternal' and that he has always been with you and always will be.*

The Gift is in the Present

His gift to you is a small golden book bound with 'the souls of evermore'. You clasp it gently in your hands and he tells you that it is time to write your destiny. On each page is a heading with a different timespan asking what you would do with your life if you had 30 years left to live, 10 years, 5 years and so on — going down to 1 minute. He asks you to write down all the things you would want to do or achieve, have, be, say or experience. He tells you to include places you want to go and people you would like to meet or see again. Whatever it is you dream of doing, no matter how small, write it here in The Book of Time. *You open the first page and begin to write:*

★ **If you had thirty years to live – what would you do with your life?**

★ **If you had ten years to live – what would you do with your life?**

★ **If you had five years to live – what would you do with your life?**

★ **If you had one year to live – what would you do with your life?**

★ **If you had one month to live – what would you do with your life?**

★ **If you had one week to live – what would you do with your life?**

★ **If you had one day to live – what would you do with your life?**

★ **If you had one minute to live – what would you do with your life?**

What did you notice about this exercise? Did you find it easy to do or did it take some time to identify all that you wanted to do, say, feel, have, experience or achieve? Were certain time limits easier or more difficult than others? Did you do this exercise? If not – ask yourself why not and how you feel about not doing it. There is no right or wrong – just an ever-growing awareness of you. Were you surprised by your answers? Were you moved by your answers? Did anything happen as you went through this exercise? What did you feel? Did you include just what you wanted to do or were there 'shoulds' and 'oughts' in your answers?

The Space Between

The time between our birth and our death is a gift and this exercise can highlight just what's really important to you. It is the space between that counts. What do you value? Are there dreams that you have yet to make happen? Is there unfinished business in any area of your life? What did you do when you only had a day left to live – what was important to you then? How did you spend your last minute on this earth and how did you feel?

Take a few moments to reflect on your answers – you have all the time you need. Rejoin the journey when you are ready.

3.
Travelling Light

As you close The Book of Time *and hand it back to the wizard you suddenly find yourself sitting in a small boat in the middle of what appears to be an endless ocean.*

'Welcome to the Sea of Change,' a small high-pitched voice calls. You look around, bewildered. 'Where are you?' you reply.

'I'm right here in front of you!' the voice continues and as you look down you see a tiny adorable lemon-coloured mouse with a mohican haircut, lime-green jodhpurs and black biker boots peering up at you with bright, inquisitive eyes.

You feel a giggle of delight begin to bubble up within you as the mouse introduces himself, 'My name is Dr Herbert de Clutterer and I am here to row you to the other side of the "Sea of Change" — pleased to meet you.'

You can't believe that you're talking to a mouse with a mohican, but you reply that you're pleased to meet him too. He tells you that he lives on the banks of the ancient river Feng Shui and it is his life's work to help people cross the infamous Sea of Change. As he says this, he takes up his oars and begins to row but within seconds he turns around, puts his paws firmly on his haunches and says breathlessly, 'It's no good — it'll have to go!' You look around and ask what exactly will have to go, to which the mouse points at all the suitcases, bags and boxes by your side.

'All of that baggage — I can't row you to the other side unless you clear the body clutter you're travelling with!' You look around and say in an amazed voice, 'I didn't know I had packed so much but I'm willing to get rid of it if it means we can travel faster.'

Herbert de Clutterer smiles a mousy kind of grin, winks and tells

*you to follow his instructions — after all, he is the king of the river
'Feng Shui' and clutter clearing is his speciality . . .
He hands you a notebook and tells you to work through it in your
own time.*

Spring-Clean Your Thoughts – Feng Shui for Mind and Spirit

Any journey we undertake is a lot easier if we travel light – the
same applies to healing and developing a healthier, more confident
and positive self-image.

Mind clutter can accumulate in the form of negative, unpleasant,
unkind or just unhelpful thoughts which you may have about
your self.

Unfortunately, after a while this way of thinking can become
habitual and you may not even be aware of all the ways in which
you talk or think negatively about yourself. Begin to clear your
mind clutter by listing the negative thoughts and beliefs you have
about your body and your self.

Include any compulsive, ritualistic or addictive thought patterns
you may have. List these under the five following headings: Personal,
Social, Career/Work, Relationships and Dreams and Inner Visions.

List them all – don't hold back and don't allow any of them to
slip by unnoticed.

> ★ **Personal** Include here your innermost thoughts about you
> and your body. What have you said about yourself either
> now or in the past that has hurt you, brought you down or
> been unkind to who you are?

> ★ **Social** Include here any worries or concerns about going
> out, meeting new people or engaging in new social
> activities, ie clubs and groups. How do your thoughts
> about your body prevent you from being more socially
> active?

★ **Career/Work** List the ways in which you feel having a
negative or low body image affects your job/work or
career prospects. Have you ever not put yourself forward
for a particular job because of the way you look (or
perceive yourself to look)?

★ **Relationships** How does feeling unconfident or not loving
your body affect all your relationships – family, sexual and
work?

★ **Dreams and Inner Visions** Describe how negative body
image worries stop you from living your dreams and
following your own inner visions. How do you prevent
yourself from living your life to the fullest or doing the
things you want to do?

After reading through your list, write across the entire page in huge
letters the word 'DELETED!'

Symbolically, you are getting rid of all that excess baggage and
are instructing your mind that this is something you no longer
wish to carry around with you. You are now free to travel unencum-
bered. It is your choice if you want to pick up your negative baggage
again but if you find it returning in the form of thoughts, worries,
dislikes, etc just come back to this page and see that it has gone –
you have already deleted it. Do this whenever you need to. It's a
powerful clearing affirmation.

Body Chi – Feng Shui for Your Body

You can clear your own body clutter and release your body's Chi
(energy or life force) by loving your body enough to attend to any
part of you that needs extra care, just as we fix any items that are
broken or don't work properly in our homes. Our bodies need to
maintain optimum health and vitality in order for our energy to
flow without obstruction.

Feng Shui masters advocate not leaving anything in the home

which needs to be mended or fixed in some way. The energy of these objects is broken and fragmented – rather like a short circuit in electrical wiring. The electricity is still flowing but its power cannot be seen. It is the same with our bodies – any break in our circuits or parts that are left uncared for may cause overall disharmony within the whole. When one part of us is out of balance the rest of our body feels the discord and we may notice that we are low in energy or feel depressed, lethargic or lacking in motivation.

Write down anything that you need to do to show your body you love it and when you are going to do this. Remember, your actions need to back up your words, as your body still won't know you love it if you don't show it. Include here anything from going to the dentist or having your cholesterol checked, to booking yourself in for a relaxing aromatherapy massage. The only person you hurt by not doing it is you! Make your word your law and put your body and your self first.

	My body needs:	Body Action – when and where
1		
2		
3		
4		
5		
6		
7		
8		
9		
10		

Body Hoarding

Do you have any old fitness videos, gym equipment, beauty/skin lotions or gimmicky diet products that are left lying around the house or stored away in cupboards and never see the light of day? Maybe you used them once or twice but now you just sneak past them feeling guilty that you haven't made their acquaintance in a while!

Are your wardrobes full of clothes that don't fit, don't suit, or are out of date (but you're waiting until hotpants come back in again)? Do you love all the clothes you have or do you just put up with them? Are you waiting until you lose some weight to buy yourself a new outfit or some sensual underwear? If so, you are giving your body mixed messages and adding to your own sense of body confusion. Every time you pass the lonely exercise bike in the spare bedroom or catch sight of a wardrobe full of unworn clothes, you keep your body and life in a holding pattern. By not using the equipment, wearing the clothes or working out with all those old fitness videos, you are causing yourself to remain in conflict with the 'should' lurking behind your thoughts. You don't really want to get on the bike – but you know that you 'should'!

The general rule here is that if you don't use it – lose it!

Only keep the things that your body loves to do and enjoy – the others can go. Get rid of the bike and get a mini trampoline instead, or replace it with nothing! Just enjoy the extra space it gives you. Do what you want and not what you 'should'.

Power Walk Your Talk

Essentially it's about making sure that your words and actions are speaking the same language. When who you are is supported by what you do (or don't do) then the dialogue flows and communication is clear and enjoyable. When what you do is not supported by what's around you then conflict results as communication breaks down.

Write down any items, under the following headings, which you have had for over a year but have not used or will not use again. (These items are all connected with the body.)

You may need physically to go and check in your cupboards, wardrobes or bathroom cabinet to discover what needs to be cleared. Take the time to do this and list your findings here in the form of an inventory. As you continue the journey, you can come back to this page and tick off all the items that you manage to get rid of or replace with something which is more 'you'. (Add in more pages if you need them.)

★ **Beauty/skin care** Include any firming/toning preparations, massage products, make-up you never use, electrical gadgets, etc.

★ **Fitness equipment** Include items such as fitness videos, exercise bikes, rowing machines, steps, weights, resistance bands, heartrate monitors, pedometers, tennis/badminton racquets, walking boots, etc.

★ **Clothes** Include anything too small, too big, too old or too uninspiring!

★ **Specific foods/drinks** Include any diet food supplements or drinks that you have in your cupboard but do not use, also any pills, diet sheets or body-building/fat-reducing formulas. Include any food or drink that you think you 'should' have but really do not enjoy.

Other People's Clutter

Refuse to take on any more body clutter by screening yourself from remarks, comments, opinions and judgements made by other people. If it is not valid, helpful, constructive or useful in any way do not take it on board.

Begin to clear away any body debris left by other people by identifying any negative or limiting ways in which others have referred to you – even if it was just in fun when they thought you would laugh. For example, one of my nicknames as a child was 'Flabby', and whilst it was meant as a term of endearment it did nothing for my sense of self-esteem or how I saw myself.

Write down any nicknames, comments, beliefs or judgements that family members, friends or colleagues have made about you which have contributed to any feelings of inadequacy about yourself. Clients often tell me that it was the negative remarks and judgements made by school teachers that hurt the most. The inner feeling was that they must be right as they were in positions of authority and clearly knew better! Many people are still trying to shake off that life sentence, pronounced upon them in their teens, of not being good enough.

I remember going to see my careers officer at school who nearly fell off her chair laughing when I told her that I wanted to dance. Okay, I happened to be around 15 stone at the time and didn't resemble the dancer's classical image, but in her mind there was no room for possibilities as she handed me a batch of secretarial leaflets and local job opportunities that she thought I would be better suited for!

For every comment or remark you list, write your own antidote alongside it. For instance, if a family member said that you would never amount to much, your antidote might be, 'I am my own person. I have my own unique talents and abilities – my life is what I make it.'

	Comments:	My Antidotes:
Family	_____	_____
Friends	_____	_____
Colleagues	_____	_____
Professionals/ Teachers/ Trainers, etc	_____	_____

The Ghost of Woman Past

It is not only words that add to our sense of body clutter but remnants from the past that we may have stored deep within our tissues, muscles and cells. Whenever we notice tension or pain in any area of our bodies the message is there – calling us to nurture, love and respond to the area of hurt and understand the message it brings. Our bodies may be visible examples of our past as we choose to carry what has been and gone. Without realizing it our bodies may continue to keep our past firmly in the present as we find it difficult to let go of people, possessions, feelings, learned behavioural patterns and beliefs.

I realized that I had never fully mourned my father's death – he died when I was a child. In the years following I held him close to me and kept his memory alive in my own physical form. I had always been told how much I looked like him – I had his eyes, his smile, his hair and even his weight! (At times I wondered what was truly mine.) I also had a terrifying fear that I would die the same way he had done – dropping dead of a heart attack at 35 years old! I was thankful when I passed the age of 35 and was still alive. In learning to love my body and clear my own body clutter I understood that my weight held the key to how I dealt with loss. In hating my body and punishing it I could express my feelings of pain at myself but also indirectly at my father who I so resembled. As I learned to love and look after me I allowed myself to express my feelings without turning the rage inwards.

Who or What are you Carrying in Your Body?

Answer the following questions (adapted from the excellent book *Transforming Body Image* by Marcia Germaine Hutchinson) by being aware of the first thought, feeling, impression or physical sensation which occurs for you. If there is no immediate response, leave the question and just allow it to 'float' in the air. Come back to it later.

1 Where in your body is your past located?
2 Where in your body is your joy located?
3 Where in your body is your sadness located?
4 Where in your body is your love located?
5 Where in your body is your present located?
6 Where in your body is your anger located?
7 Where in your body is your happiness located?
8 Where in your body is your future located?
9 Where in your body is your mother located?
10 Where in your body is your father located?
11 Where in your body are your sisters/brothers located?
12 Where in your body is your guilt located?
13 Where in your body is your fear located?
14 Where in your body is your shame located?
15 Where in your body is your freedom located?

This exercise may just give you some clues to any areas which carry tension or where you store emotions. For example, if you are aware that you hold your fear in your shoulders then as soon as you feel tension in this area you can ask yourself what that fear is. I know that I hold fear in my stomach and used to try and quell that fear by eating down my feelings (literally). Knowing that it is fear I am experiencing gives me the key to unlock what that fear is. Instead of trying to push it down I try to listen to what it has to say and in that moment I connect my body and my mind in the loving presence of my spirit.

> *You notice that Herbert mouse is smiling at you as you finish writing your answers and he tells you that you have just one more thing to do before you can cross the 'Sea of Change.'*
> *You look up and tell him that you are ready.*
> *He winds his long tail around him as he tells you that this task is sometimes the hardest of all and many people never take the time to complete it fully or even to begin it in the first place. You ask what it could be and his nose twitches the air in a sensitive manner.*
> *'The next task is about saying goodbye and moving on,' he says*

gently. 'Sometimes this is the hardest thing to do, especially when it means letting go of parts of yourself.'

Before you can speak he tells you that he would like you to write a letter to your body explaining why you are embarking on this journey of body confidence and love and how you feel about leaving your old ways of thinking, feeling and being behind. He asks you to tell your body what you are looking forward to in terms of feeling good about your body and your self, and how you wish to feel and be. If there are things that you will miss or are afraid of then include these in your letter. Finally, he asks you to tell your body how long you will be travelling and what you will take with you.

In essence, this letter calls you to acknowledge the part or parts of you that have always held you back. They may be your most negative beliefs and fears that have held you gripped in body dislike, hate, shame or rage. The message they bring is almost always that you are not good enough in some way, shape or form and that you need to be something or someone else in order to be loved, successful and accepted.

They have found their expression and power in how you have felt or feel about your body and your self. Writing the letter begins to address this imbalance and allows you to state your intentions clearly and positively in a loving way.

Write to your body as if you were writing to an old friend, telling them all about where you are in your life right now and the changes that you are making.

As I was researching through all my personal body-work files I came across the letter that I had written to my body years ago when I had first begun to make peace with my self. I would like to share it with you here.

Dear Body,

Writing a letter to you is one of the hardest things I have had to do because most of the time I don't want to see you, let alone communicate with you.

I don't know where to begin but I do know that I am so

sorry that I've hurt you and for all the pain I've caused you over the years. I think back to the abuse – the endless crash diets, the slimming pills, laxatives and the harmful way I thought about you. It just makes me want to cry.

I'm sorry that I've called you all those hurtful names – you didn't deserve it. If you were a friend of mine I would have lost you long ago – but you're still here and on some level I know that you understand why I do the things I do.

It's me that makes you ugly. I stop you from being all that you could be. I'm sorry. I have always been so ashamed of you and wished that you were different. It's not you that needs to be different – it's me! I know that I need to love, appreciate and accept you and most of all thank you. After all, I experience my life through you! I have always felt so separate from you. Perhaps this letter will help bring us closer together.

What amazes me about you is that you stay so strong and healthy in spite of what I do to you. We have been through so much pain together and I have hated you with a vengeance. I guess what I'm saying is that I hope you will forgive me – I'm working on loving you and not punishing you.

Perhaps one day we will be best friends – I would like to get to know you, understand and respect you.

Until then, please don't give up on me.

Yours

Astrid

Herbert rests his paw gently on your shoulder and tells you that it's time to say goodbye to all those old thoughts, beliefs, fears and criticisms as you step into a new world of body confidence and change.

He hugs his arms across his chest as he looks upwards at the darkening sky and knows that night is approaching with her outstretched arms clad in gothic black. Soon, even the sea will submit to her silent slumbers and only the calling voices of dreamers will be heard.

Now write your own letter – allowing yourself to express all your feelings, thoughts, dreams, pain, hurt and needs. Say all that you feel in your own way and in your own time.

This letter is important – write it if you can. If it is too difficult to write at the moment, be aware of how you feel about not writing it. What is it you want to say but won't allow yourself?

Never judge yourself for not completing any part of the journey – just become aware of where your resistances lie and the parts of you that you keep locked up or closely defended. These are often the areas that need loving the most and where your biggest changes may occur. The very parts of you that cause you the most pain are the same parts that give you the keys to unlocking your body confidence and love.

. . . And as night embraces you, holding you lovingly in her healing spell, you feel your body relax and allow a long sigh to escape from your lips. You feel as if a huge weight has been lifted from your body and mind and your eyelids grow heavy with the release of sleep. Herbert mouse smiles as you snuggle down deep into the rocking motion of the boat and begins to row you across the 'Sea of Change.'

Dreamily you ask him, 'How can you travel so fast?' to which he replies laughingly, 'Because I take myself lightly!'

And as sleep melts away your fears you feel lighter than you have felt in years and happy to be speeding across the 'Sea of Change.'

4.

The Lost Village of **Self-Belief**

Sparkles of fresh sunlight kiss your eyelids open as you awake into a new day and look around you. There is no sign of Herbert — only a rose by your side with a note attached saying, 'Travel deep into the mists of time and remember.'

You stroke the rose gently against your cheek and as you do so you notice that the early morning sea mist is closing in all around you, shrouding everything with a translucent ghostly aura.

From deep in the mist comes a shuffling sound and you try to peer beyond the white haze to see who's there. Gradually, as your eyes become accustomed to this drifting ethereal world you make out the shape of a hooded figure.

You feel no fear — only curiosity. The figure comes face to face with you, but try as you might you cannot see what he looks like as the mists are too dense.

The hooded one speaks and says that he is about to share with you one of the greatest truths of the universe if you would care to listen. You nod your head and he asks you to come and sit by the stone circle that is emerging out of the mists. Before he begins, he tells you that this is a powerful visualization which has the power to transform lives. He asks you to remember what he has said and then repeat this visualization every day or for as long as you need it.

'It will help you remember,' he says huskily.

'Remember what?' you ask.

'Who you really are,' comes the reply, and he now motions you to be still.

Read the following visualization through and then close your eyes, take several deep breaths, allowing your body to relax, and go through it again in your mind. Allow your senses to soak up the imagery of the visualization, adding in anything else that may come into your awareness, and relive it often. Just get the feel of it and of what is happening. You could also record this onto a tape and play it every day if you find it easier.

Eternally Beautiful

> Spirals of morning mist settle over the deep purple hue of the mountain. Morning is lazily edging her way across the land. The sky is a clear, clear blue and the air smells damp and fresh. The sea is pale and glittery and all around is touched with the promise of a beautiful summer's day to come.
>
> This is your day – the day you came into being.
>
> Crystallized in a tiny eggshell . . .
>
> You sleep . . .
>
> Your fragile form growing stronger with every new breath you take.
>
> The delicate pink edge of your home . . .
>
> Iridescent silver and golden, protects your softly sleeping form within.
>
> Curled up like a child butterfly, just waiting for the day to kiss you awake and shake you free.
>
> There has never been beauty such as this.
>
> In a glow of light, cracks appear in the outer edges of the shell – tiny, dry meandering lines and then . . .
>
> An opening . . .
>
> Just enough to see into.
>
> A tiny hand stretches out to touch the world.
>
> You are finally born and the shell crumples around you like soft tissue paper.
>
> You step outside and a warm breeze kisses your skin as you wake, smiling into the glow of the emerging sun.
>
> 'I am here,' you breathe.

'*I am born at last – my first day on this earth, my first second in this time.*'

Your birth guardian – a wise old sage, clad in wrinkles and an inner knowing, whispers your destiny . . .

'*You are a child of the universe – of all there is and will ever be. You are eternally beautiful, strong and proud and these are the gifts I bestow upon you . . .*

'*May you hear the sound of your own sweet breathing,*

'*And the cavernous roar of your heart,*

'*May you live a life of wonder, giving priority to your dreams,*

'*May your eyes see beauty in every darkest place,*

'*May you dance your vision into someone's heart and touch them with your presence.*

'*But most of all –*

'*May you remember how beautiful, perfect and loved you are for all eternity.*'

As the hooded one finishes speaking you realize that he is your birth guardian from the visualization. And as the mists begin to clear you gaze into his loving eyes, basking in the wisdom within.

He speaks quietly as he heads you away from the stone circle, '*You need to remember the eternal truth – that each and every one of us is born beautiful, sacred, perfect and loved. Unfortunately, by the time most of us leave childhood we have already forgotten who we really are, the gifts we have to share and the love we have to give and receive. We wander so far away from our own truth that the rest of our lives are spent trying to find the way back home. When people look in the mirror they don't see the beauty of their spirit shining out or feel each and every heavenly cell giggling with life and happiness in their bodies. They are too busy comparing or screaming insults and disappointments to understand that love is a slow realization of the beauty within.*'

You take his hands gently in yours as he says sadly, '*It's not their fault – they just forgot. You are one of the lucky ones – remember your truth and you will always be home.'*

Before your birth guardian leaves he tells you that he has a gift for you but that you must choose it for yourself. As he speaks he offers you the choice of the following things:

A key
A sound
A wish

He tells you that the meaning of the gift will be revealed in due time and that all you need to know is that it will help you in your quest for body confidence and love.

Write down the gift you have chosen – go with the first thought or feeling you had when reading this.

The gift I have chosen is

_____

The mists of time roll away to reveal a golden sunkissed evening. 'I love this time of day,' you breathe as ribbons of shadowy light weave their patterns across your eyes.

'Days such as these must be remembered for always,' you sigh to yourself as you begin to walk down an old worn-out pathway leading to what the signpost calls 'The Lost Village of Self-Belief'. The road winds down, twisting its way around forgotten bends and long-lost flowers until you see the village — ramshackle, overgrown and hauntingly beautiful!

One faded cottage seems to call to you through its broken windowpanes and, as you approach, the neglected roses in the driveway tell the story — no one is home. No one's been home for years. You shudder with sadness, as you know that the postman never brings news of any kind to its door. On black cold nights you will see no glimmer of warmth shining from the windows. Seasons pass unnoticed and life seems to have stopped — that is, until the moment that you arrive . . . when all of a sudden a distant thudding like a sleeper's heartbeat can be heard coming from the depths of the house. Somewhere deep inside, life is returning.

Suddenly, the house shudders as a sudden breeze blows the top window shut and you step backwards, straight into the arms of a phantom-like man with milky-white teeth and a face like a sheet of ice. The heartbeat of the house must have alerted him to your presence.

As you compose yourself he draws his long black cloak around his skeletal frame and tells you that he is the Keeper of the Chains. It is his job to bind, tether, restrain and hold back by the power of fear anything that is remotely special, loved, unique, fantastic, gorgeous or alive in any way.

He is an energy vampire and his life's work is sucking out the life force – making sure that things remain stuck, lifeless and controllable.

He tells you that the only way you can break free from your chains is to write your own body myth. He hands you a story which has blank spaces for you to fill in your own words.

Fill in the blank spaces with either a positive or negative adjective (describing word). Go with the first words that come into your mind. Do not spend too long on this – allow your energy to flow with the story.

(PDW) = Positive Describing Word
(NDW) = Negative Describing Word

The Body Myth

Once upon a time in a land of chains lived a (PDW) _____ warrior princess. She knew that she was magical even though the Keepers of the Chains told her that she was just a

(NDW) _____ nobody!
Day after day she would try to tell the other inhabitants of the

land that they were all really special and deserved to be free, but they laughed at her, thinking that she was mad.

That is – until one day an old woman whispered to her secretly, 'Maybe you are right my dear – to tell the truth I've always thought I was a bit special too but was too scared to say so.'

The warrior princess was delighted and said with excitement, 'Everyone is special in their own way and we've just been led to believe that we are (NDW) _____ to keep us down.' She carried on enthusiastically, 'Surely it is our turn to shine after all these years of living in darkness. We have felt (NDW) _____ for so long – but not any more!'

And with that the old woman and the warrior princess began talking to the people of the village telling them their beliefs and how (PDW) _____ each and every person was.

Unfortunately, one black and thunderous night the Keepers of the Chains heard the rumour that people were beginning to feel good about themselves and (PDW) _____. And their fury turned to anger!

Within seconds they had descended upon the princess, dragging her out of her rosy little house and out onto the black fields of despair. She hugged her old woollen shawl more closely around her shaking shoulders and watched in fear as the Keepers pointed to the blackened sky on which they flashed up in words of lightning: 'You are not a warrior – you are what we tell you and we tell you that you are:

(NDW) _____

(NDW) _____

(NDW) _____

(NDW) _____

(NDW) _____ '

By now a huge crowd had gathered and there was silence as the warrior princess stood taller and prouder than ever before and looked steadily at the Keepers of the Chains.

'I am none of what you have just said – I am who I am and I am:

(PDW) _____

(PDW) _____

(PDW) _____

(PDW) _____

(PDW) _____ '

The crowd gasped and a grumbling rumble could be felt through the earth as one chain after another began to creak and break.

The Keepers looked around wildly as one by one more voices could be heard joining the voice of the warrior princess – each crying out who they really were – not afraid to shine in their own glorious light. And as each one cried out their uniqueness another chain broke – chains that had bound their bodies, houses, wishes, dreams, fantasies, lives and their very souls.

After you have completed 'The Body Myth' write out all the negative describing words you used on the left and all the positive words on the right.

	Binding Words Words that chain you:	**Key Words** Words to set you free:
1	_____	_____
2	_____	_____
3	_____	_____
4	_____	_____
5	_____	_____
6	_____	_____
7	_____	_____
8	_____	_____

All the positive words you selected are your **key words!** These words are powerful for you and will unlock your own body confidence. Allow these words to become a part of your everyday life. Use them in conversation and think of them often when referring to yourself. Meditate or visualize them becoming a part of you – flowing through your whole being. These are words that will set you free. Each word is like a mini-affirmation of who you are. Write them out on a piece of paper and carry them with you.

Be aware also of the words that bind you. These are the words that will hold you back – keep you down. Be on your guard for them and if one sneakily manages to creep into your conversation, thoughts or beliefs – call upon your key words to vanquish the demon! Replace the words that bind with words that heal and you have the key (literally) to ultimate body and self-confidence.

Become a Vampire Slayer!

Who or what are your own 'energy vampires'? Bring them into the light of day as you identify all the things, people, situations, activities, foods, drinks and places that bring you down, drain you of energy or make you feel numb or depressed in any way. Write down anything that drains your own life force and the feeling you have when you experience this. Just as the character Buffy in the TV series slays her demons with a magical blend of kickboxing, martial arts and a superhuman force, you can slay yours with understanding, identification and a resolve to remove them from your life.

We all know people who drain our energy or make us feel low minutes after meeting them – they are usually fairly easy to spot. What are often a lot harder to see are the hidden vampires that we find in our places of work, the daily situations we find ourselves in or the foods we eat. Try and identify anything that brings you down, makes you feel weak, powerless, drained or depressed and the possible reasons why. Ask yourself who or what sucks away your self-belief and how you allow this to happen.

My Energy Vampires are:

	Vampire	Feeling	Reason
People	_____	_____	_____
Situations	_____	_____	_____
Places	_____	_____	_____
Activities	_____	_____	_____
Foods/Drinks	_____	_____	_____

As you finish bringing your energy vampires out into the light of day there is a blinding flash and the Keeper of the Chains disappears in a cloud of dirty grey smoke.

Darkness seems to be quickening now and shadows appear aimlessly here and there, unsure of where to linger. The cottage calls to you as your eyes are drawn to a tiny wooden, rusted front door, warped with the years and aged with time. To you it is the most beautiful door you have ever seen. As you touch the old woodwork carvings around the letterbox you feel the depths of years gone by.

'How I love this house,' you breathe.

'And we love you,' the house whispers back and the door creaks open a fraction.

As you reach out to push the door wider two white owls appear by your side and a note flutters down from their beaks. You smile at the brown-eyed fluffy ones and begin to read the note:

Self-Belief is a Choice

'Welcome to the Village of Lost Self-Belief. We hoped you would come to help us live again and find our self-belief once more. You are about to enter the house of choices. Each choice you make will determine how you feel and subsequently how you act towards your body and your self. To make this fun we have devised a quiz for you to answer. Just read the questions, make your choice and then write down your feelings. The quiz takes you through the house but it is up to you what you

choose to find there. Remember there are no right or wrong answers – whatever you answer is right for you. Good luck and enjoy!'

Answer the questions by choosing the first thoughts or images that come into your mind. Answer as spontaneously as you can and then go to Part Two of the Body Confidence Quest and fill in more details about your answers. Only go to Part Two when Part One has been answered.

The Body Confidence Quest –
Part One

1   Imagine that you are standing outside the faded cottage. Your first question is, do you wish to change the exterior of the cottage and make it into another type of building? You have four choices:
    a   Leave it as the country cottage
    b   Change it to a stately home
    c   Change it to a church
    d   State another type of building of your own choice

2   Imagine now that you are standing in front of your chosen building – just about to go inside. Your hand is on the doorknob and as you turn it and walk inside you are aware that you feel:
    a   Apprehensive
    b   Excited
    c   Okay – neither one way or the other
    d   State any other feeling that comes to mind

3   As you walk inside the hallway you find the following:
    a   Nothing but floorboards – it's completely empty
    b   A patterned rug, flowers on a hall table and pictures on the walls
    c   It's full of people, animals, a cosy fire and a chair
    d   State anything else you imagine to be there

4　There are four possible directions for you to go in the house. Choose which way you will go.
  a　To the left
  b　To the right
  c　Straight ahead
  d　Upstairs

5　As you travel in the direction you have chosen you come across a door which is marked 'The Body Store'. You walk into the room and find:
  a　It is full of shop dummies and mannequins
  b　Exercise equipment and weighing scales
  c　Nothing at all
  d　State your own choice

6　You can change this room if you would like to. If so, state the changes you would choose to make:
  a　Candles and an open log fire
  b　A table full of food and drink
  c　A jacuzzi
  d　Comfortable furniture
  e　Huge windows with beautiful curtains
  f　Someone you know – a friend maybe
  g　Music
  h　You do not choose to change the room
  i　State other changes you would make which are not listed

7　You leave the room and walk back into the hallway. Saying goodbye to the house you walk out and close the front door behind you. As you leave you see that in front of you is a high wall. And as you look for a way out you notice a gate straight in front of you with a note attached. It tells you:

'This is a magic gate and the only way for you to open it is to use the gift that was given to you by your birth guardian when you first arrived in the village. What did you choose?'

Write down your choice of gift here . . . I open the gate with:

a A key

b A sound

c A wish

The Body Confidence Quest –
Part Two

Now go back through your answers and fill in more detail about them here. Allow your imagination to really come into play and write as much as you can about the choices you have made.

1 Describe the building you chose including stonework, condition of the building, if it is alone or close to others, any colours or other details your building has. Is it old or new, imposing or hidden? Create it all here.

2 What did you feel just as you were about to walk inside? Explain the feeling. If you were apprehensive, what were you apprehensive about? If you were excited describe the excitement. What was making you feel excited? If you felt nothing write down how nothing felt.

3 Describe in more detail the features that were in the hallway. Include colours, any fabrics, the condition of the hallway and if you chose people to be there – who were they?

4 Describe why you chose to go in the direction you took. Why did you choose this way and not the others? What prompted your choice?

5 Describe in as much detail as you can what you found in 'The Body Store' and what you liked about it. Include especially how going into the room made you feel.

6 Write down here the changes you made to this room (if any). Again, describe these changes in as much detail as

you can. Also, why did you make the changes and how did you feel after you had made them?

7 Describe why you chose the gift and what that gift means to you. For example, if you selected the key, write down what the key looked like – was it large or small, new or old, rusted or in prime condition? If the sound was your choice then what sound was it? Was it many sounds or is there just one that you are aware of? If, however, you chose the wish as your gift, describe what the wish was. What were you wishing for? What could wishing bring you – why choose the wish over the other two?

As you finish the Body Confidence Quest the two owls soar into flight above your head and you blow them a kiss as they leave. Just as you are wondering what the quest meant you notice that the village seems to have changed. There are lights flickering in the houses and a sense of someone being home.

You realize that you are so very tired and the light from the cottage seems to beckon you in. As you enter the hallway, the house sighs and draws you into its protective embrace, leading you up the rickety wooden staircase. Right in front of you is a most beautiful room – the room of your dreams with the most beautiful, comfortable bed right in the middle. As you allow your body to become seduced by the deep softness of the bed, the sounds of the night rock you to sleep whilst the bed adjusts itself around your body, moulding itself to your very shape and form.

'We love you,' the house croons as you fall into the sleep of knowing. As you sleep, you dream of the Body Confidence Quest that you have just been on and you ask for the meanings of the questions.

The Body Confidence Quest Unwrapped

The Body Confidence Quest is designed to provoke your own images, thoughts, feelings and fantasies about your innermost self. It is a way to access parts of you that usually remain hidden, lost, suppressed or are just forgotten about as you delve into the world of your subconscious. Read your answers back, as the meaning of each question becomes clear. Each choice you made refers to how you see yourself on an inner level and by the use of symbols, image work and a gently guided journey you may discover the keys to unlocking your own doors of body confidence and love. Allow your thoughts and feelings to explore what you have written and be aware of any flashes of insight or understanding in the days to come. This quest may be taken again and again and it is fascinating to see how the answers change as people develop. Do not worry if the meaning is not immediately clear – sometimes you just need to allow some space for the subconscious mind to filter the thoughts, images and feelings. Very often the answers will come in your dreams. And remember, these interpretations are a guideline only. Even if you disagree with the explanation, it's what it means to you that's important.

The Meanings of the Questions

Question One: The Exterior of the Building

The exterior of the building refers to the 'you' that you show to the outside world. In essence, it is the exterior you. Read your detailed answer and see if there are any similarities between the building you have chosen and yourself or how you represent yourself outwardly.

A client was amazed to find that the building she had chosen was a stately home. She had described her home as grand, imposing, detached and magnificent. People had to pay to come in and the stonework needed some upkeep.

She laughed as she applied that image to herself and said, 'I guess I am like that stately home. I give off this air of being confident and in control and a bit austere! I don't allow people to get too close to me – they have to prove themselves first. I suppose also that I've let myself go a bit and I could do with a bit of love and attention too!'

Another client selected the church, which she described as sacred, a place of worship, cold and steeped in history, faith and religious order. When she looked at how this might apply to her she could see similarities. She did feel that her body was a sacred place but she also felt that she had lived her life under a strict control handed down to her by her parents and their parents before them.

How does your description relate to the exterior 'you'?

Question Two: About to Enter the House

This refers to how you feel about the inner you. Are you excited, apprehensive or just okay about getting to know the inner you and what you may discover? In what ways do your feelings reflect how you feel about getting to know parts of yourself that you may have kept hidden?

Question Three: The Hallway

What you find in the hallway refers to the inner you. What did you find as you looked inside? One client said that she found the hallway to be full of people and she realized that this was representative of how she felt about herself. She said, 'I do feel full up, like I have everyone else's thoughts, opinions and ideas running around inside of me – I don't know where mine are!'

Another client found that there was just empty space, which she recognized as herself. She told me, 'I've done a lot of work on me already. I eat well, have regular relaxing body treatments and have tried to come to terms with how I feel about myself. Perhaps the space is what I need now.'

Whatever you feel about the choice you have made, it is right for you. There are no definitive answers in this quest – only the answers you come up with.

Question Four: Directions

Which direction did you choose to take? How did you make your choice? Generally, the directions indicate where you need to do the most healing and which area of your life needs the most focus, love and attention.

'Left' indicates that you need to look at your past for your answers or that you may live too much in the past. Go with your first feelings about what is right for you. Perhaps you need to heal and let go of the past before you can move on. It also suggests that you need to follow your own intuition and connect with your creative and artistic nature. Choosing the left side also indicates a need for emotional expression, perhaps by releasing the past and allowing your self to receive love, nurturing and comfort in the present.

'Right' indicates that you are looking to the future for your answers – how you want to feel and be. Alternatively, you are living too much in the future and not enough in the 'now'. Choosing this direction also indicates a need for you to become actively involved in whatever you are doing. It highlights a need for you to become passionate about your day-to-day reality and work assertively and practically on the changes you want to make.

'Straight ahead' shows that your healing and work lie directly in front of you. It is what is present at this very moment in time. It may highlight a need for you to look at what is happening in your life right now and to live in the moment.

'Upstairs' shows that you are looking to your higher self to help you in your quest. This area is deeply connected to intuition, spirituality and a feeling of becoming one with all there is – the universe. This direction may be showing you where you need to look for your divine guidance and inspiration. How does this area manifest in your life?

Question Five: The Body Store

This refers to the thoughts, ideals and images you have about your body and how you 'should' treat it. What have you stored up about your body? The body store gives clues to your relationship with your body. One client found this quite scary as she said that her body store was full of bodies with no heads! When she thought about this she realized that it was exactly how she felt – disconnected! She said that she always lived in her head and never showed any feelings. She intellectualized, theorized and analysed but never showed any emotion of any kind. Her body felt stiff, rigid and inflexible and she realized that she needed to connect her mind, body and spirit in her search for body confidence and love. When I first did this exercise I had nothing in my body store which surprised me at first, but later I realized that I needed to look at what was missing from my relationship with my body.

Question Six: Body Store Changes

The changes you made (if any) to this room indicate what you need to help you move past your own body lock. If you chose to add candles and an open fire, ask what this means to you – what kind of atmosphere do they help create? If you chose music – what music did you choose? Was it a classical piece steeped in power, emotion and played by a full orchestra? Or maybe it was a melodic love song, or perhaps a rap tune that brings out the street kid in you!

If you chose the table full of food and drink, look at the food you have selected and what it means to you. Is it comfort food or something you would order when eating out in a lovely restaurant? Is it sweet or spicy? Is it hot or cold? How does the food and drink make you feel? Is it food you would normally eat or something quite exotic? As with all the examples it is what they mean or represent to you that counts. Don't try too hard to find a meaning, just let your mind and imagination flow around the objects you chose and be open to any thoughts, feelings or insights this may bring.

If a jacuzzi was one of your choices then look at what having a jacuzzi in your room would mean to you. Is it a luxury? Does it make you feel pampered and sensuous? Perhaps this choice is telling you that you need to take more time to give yourself treats or that you just need some time out.

If comfortable furniture was your choice you may need to spend some more time relaxing and feeling comfortable with being you. Perhaps you literally need to sit down, put your feet up and be alone with you. This may also indicate that you need to avoid distractions in your life, as when we are truly comfortable somewhere we fully enjoy being where we are and do not look for things to distract us.

If you chose huge windows then you may be on the verge of making some major changes in your life and within yourself or you may have already experienced them. This choice indicates that you are ready to look deeper into accepting who you are and having confidence in what you see, feel, think and do. You are letting the light of awareness into your room and in doing so you begin to see clearly. Ask yourself what you want to see out of your windows and reflect on the answer you come up with.

Choosing someone to be in your room indicates that you may need more support, help or reassurance in what you are doing. Ask yourself who that person is and what they mean to you. Also, look at areas where you may need help from other people to enable you to achieve your goals. How about joining a group or club? Or perhaps it would help to look into different types of therapies to support you in your journey. Maybe you just need more support from your family and need to tell them how they can help you.

Look at any changes you made and what they mean to you. Do they soothe or comfort you or make you feel wild and excited?

The lady who had felt disconnected in the previous example changed her body store image by connecting the heads to the bodies. This was a huge step in her own healing as she mentally gave herself permission to feel through her body and not stay locked up in her head.

What can you learn from your changes?

Question Seven: Opening the Gate

The gate here represents your own gateway to body love and confidence and the ways it will help you access your own inner magic.

Calling upon the gifts you chose earlier in the journey gives you a clue to what may be helpful to you.

The key calls you to find what fits you and not what you fit into. There is a sense of activity and purpose here as there is only one key which will open the gate. It demands that you choose your own way in your own time and walk your own path. When you find what is uniquely yours and wear it with pride you will open the gateway to your own power. Look at the key words of your Body Myth and use them often. Be active and proactive in how you travel your journey. The key demands that you put your thoughts, ideas and dreams into action. It's no good just putting the key into the lock, you have to turn it to open it – turn the key and turn your life around.

The sound asks you to tune into yourself on a high intuitive level and really listen to what you say, need, feel, think, believe or do. What is your sound? Is it a sound you know or a sound that you can't describe? The sound calls you to follow your soul's calling. It asks you to hear your own inner voice and have faith and trust in your body's deepest wisdom. Sound shows you the ways to open the gate to the immense power and strength you have inside. It calls you (literally) to communicate your needs, dreams and beliefs in a powerfully positive way. It asks you to hear your own words and make them your creed. Its message is to make heard what is on the inside – outside. Essentially, it calls you to stand up for who you are and speak your own truth.

The wish calls you to remember your dreams, visions and fantasies. These may be your personal ways to open the gateway to deep body love. The wish asks you to soar above any pain or unhappiness you have felt and take a trip over the rainbow. It calls you to invoke your imagination and wildest dreams of what and who you can be. Like a child it demands that you believe in your own power and magic and play again with make believe! Wishes are about seeing – see yourself as beautiful. Open your eyes to your own incredible beauty! Thoughts are powerful and what you wish for will become you. Go on – drift along on a warm breeze, laugh as they take you seriously and fall asleep on a dusky moonbeam!

As you slumber, bathed in moonlight and longings, the house smiles and wraps its loving arms closer around you, holding you safe.

In the distance the two fluffy white owls hoot with pleasure as they sit perched on a signpost that now reads 'The Village of Self-Belief – not lost anymore'. They sing as the moon winks from behind a cloud.

5.

Sabotage City

Soft, warm drops of rain, sprinkling lightly on your face, wake you suddenly. You sit up quickly, realizing that the house and the village have disappeared and that you are nestled snugly under the most magnificent weeping willow tree you have ever seen.

All around you the storm clouds are gathering and you look with concern at the ever-darkening sky.

In the distance you can just make out some huge irregular shapes and you decide to run towards them, thinking that it may be a town or village where you can find some shelter. As you get closer, you realize that it's not a town at all but immense boulders, one on top of another, that are blocking your way. Cut deep into the rocks are the words 'Sabotage City' — rather like the 'Hollywood' sign in Los Angeles only less welcoming! There appears to be no way through, as the craggy outcrops seem to be miles wide and dominate the skyline like colossal skyscrapers of granite. A sense of despair wells up inside you as you realize you have come so far only to be greeted by this!

As you stand there shaking with the chill of the summer rain on your skin, you feel defeated and prepare to turn back.

*'**Name us**,' comes a low guttural voice from one of the stones. You turn back sharply, convinced you must be going mad.*

*'**Name us**,' the voice calls out again. '**If you name us we will move out of your way and let you pass.**'*

You answer back feeling tired and despondent. 'But I don't know your names — I could spend a million years guessing and still never get it right!'

There is a dark snigger that seems to echo through and around the stones as they appear to rock with amusement.

'**You know us!**' *they all clamour,* '**It was you who created us!**'

Now you are really baffled. 'How did I create you?'

The stones brood a little and then in slithery, slimy voices they chant in unison: **You created us through every dark thought and through every unkind, unhelpful, hurtful, damaging or careless words you have ever said about yourself. We were born the day you forgot to trust you and put yourself last on your list for love. We grew in stature every time you thought you couldn't do something or backed down from being you. You made us what we are today!**'

Horrified, you cry out, 'But I don't want you – you are blocking my way – LET ME THROUGH!'

The stones seem to huddle closer together like bent, black witches gathering around a midnight cauldron. They repeat again in voices like distant thunder, '**Name us and we will clear your path.**'

Body Blocks

We all create our own saboteurs – the stones that weigh us down physically, mentally or emotionally, and provide reasons why we can't do, be or live our lives the way we dream. In terms of body confidence we need to meet, recognize and learn to gently challenge these wanton hinderers from within and the illusions they bring.

Inside all of us are so many different 'I's – so many seemingly conflicting parts that each appear to have their own identity, needs and demands. There is the 'I' that wants to get out into the world and proudly display its talents, the 'I' that wants to snuggle in quietly and nod by the fireside, the 'I' that has dreams of escaping the 'rat race' and renovating an old farmhouse in Tuscany, and the 'I' that simply wants to rest, relax and do nothing in particular.

There are hundreds upon hundreds of them and yet all of them are 'us'. Our task is to learn to recognize which 'I' is speaking at any one time and to be aware of the feelings and emotions that this part of us evokes. For example, whenever you embark on a new diet or fitness plan you are being directed by the part of you that demands you knuckle down to some serious calorie counting and adhere to a regular workout regime.

However, lying just behind this part is another, less enthusiastic part waiting in ambush as you set out to succeed. This part may not want to conform to a diet sheet, or maybe it's the part of you that just can't be bothered. Either way, it acts as a saboteur – preventing you from getting what you want and throwing blocks in your way. Self-sabotage happens when all our different 'I's speak a different language and nobody is listening to the conversation anyway!

When you listen to and are aware of what you need and how you are feeling in the moment, you engage in a dialogue with your mind, body and spirit. When all aspects of you work towards the same outcome with the driving force of love, acceptance and understanding – that's when body magic happens and confidence is the natural result. You can truly feel confident because you know that all parts of you are singing the same tune and you are creating a state of body, mind and spirit harmony.

Yes . . . But

Becoming aware of the ways in which you stop yourself from doing, feeling or achieving what you want in life asks that you look out for your possible saboteurs and get them on your side. Behind every saboteur lies fear and it is amazing how many people use self-sabotage as a means of fear management. Instead of experiencing the fear, anxiety or stress that a particular life event brings, we prevent ourselves from having to go through that fear no matter how much we may want what lies on the other side of it. The new job we desire means we have to put ourselves through an interview and possible rejection. The art school we want to be accepted by will expect us to show our work and, again, we might be rejected. Saying that we love someone might mean that we have to open up our true feelings to another and maybe that feels too vulnerable!

For every part of us that screams out, 'YES!' there's another smaller voice tapping inside our heads, biting its lip, saying, 'BUT!' And here we have the classic 'Yes–But' syndrome.

How many times have you heard (or even said it yourself) a person saying that they would love to do something, then following their statement with an immediate 'but' that puts a block in the way?

Come Out, Come Out, Wherever you Are!

It's the same with feeling great about who you are and living in a body you enjoy. Whilst we might all stand up and yell out to the world that this is what we want, underneath that bright top note is a dull, flatter 'but' note that muffles the pure sound of our desire. The secret is to spot when that 'but' is about to appear and win him/her over to your side with soothing talk and loving actions, and by acknowledging that there is a little creature called 'fear' lurking in the shadows. Sometimes it is hard to know when we are preventing ourselves from doing what we want as our saboteurs may come dressed up as perfectly reasonable excuses for why we 'shouldn't' do something or why we would be better off not bothering. Many saboteurs hide in the realms of the subconscious and come out when you least expect them to in the form of something you say, do or experience – as in the case of illness.

A friend of mine noticed that one of her saboteurs seemed to hide out at her parents' home. No matter what good resolutions she made to feel confident and happy about herself, whenever she walked into her parents' house (the house she had lived in as a child), it was as if she was walking into 'Timewarp City'! All her good intentions would fly straight out of the window as her mother criticized her style of dress and would make comments like, 'Surely you're not planning to go out looking like that!'

She said, 'It's as if I revert to a five year old again and hand over all responsibility for me as soon as I walk through the front door. It's not my mum's fault – she's just doing what she always did and I guess in her mind I am still a child. I just wish I had more confidence to assert the woman I am today and not hide behind the child I was!' She went on, 'After spending some time at home I always find myself eating too much, feeling depressed, doubting myself and generally feeling inadequate!'

Name the Stones That Weigh you Down

How do you show your body that you don't love you? Become aware of all of the blocks you put in your way that obstruct your own sense of body confidence. Ask yourself, 'How heavy is the burden that my words lay upon my body?' or, 'How do my actions and thoughts impede my progress?' How do you distract yourself from fully loving and taking care of you? Do you find that you take care of everyone else so much that you never have any time left for your own self-care? Is guilt one of your body blocks? Do you feel guilty for trying to do something for yourself? Are you afraid that your change will affect everyone else around you? Are you scared to 'rock the boat' or do you feel that being confident about you will push everyone else's buttons?

Do you spend long hours at work so that you leave yourself exhausted and too rundown to even think about how you feel about you? Or do you prefer to live your life vicariously through the tv as you escape into a fantasy world of 'real life' soap operas, music or sport? Where does fear come into this? Are you afraid that you will lose what you already have if you change? What happens if you change and others don't? Where will that leave you? Are you brave enough to leave the body garbage club behind and become the president of your own new body confidence club?

Perhaps your biggest body barriers manifest themselves as carriers of low self-worth. Do you feel that in some way it's selfish to look after and live in a body you feel confident about? Do you give away your power by not honouring your word?

A friend of mine did this every time she tried to have half an hour's pampering time for herself. She would tell her husband and children that she was going to have a bath and did not want to be disturbed for at least half an hour. She said that she wouldn't come out of the bathroom or be available during that time – except for an emergency.

You can bet your life that as soon as the bathroom door was closed one of the children would be standing outside whimpering – desperate to use the toilet or wanting their mum for some reason. Every time this happened she opened the door and gave in to their demands, giving her own power away as her words meant less and less to her.

Short term it was easier for her to give in; however, in the back of her mind she knew that she wasn't even allowing herself to have half an hour's peace and special time for herself, which made her feel worse in the long run.

It's understandable and part of our human nature to move towards what brings us pleasure and shy away from those things which may bring us pain. However, the pain, anxiety or stress we feel may be the very thing that leads us to our ultimate growth and love for who we are. The short-term pain we stifle only goes to perpetuate long-term dissatisfaction with ourselves, as somewhere within us we know our own truth and yearn to follow our innermost callings. This is why all the weight loss in the world, or the most defined, sleek and supple body, or the most beautiful face will never bring you joy if you can't see and acknowledge the beauty within. Taking the step to love, honour, respect and listen to your body may seem hard or alien to you when your only dialogue with your self has been a slanging match!

Short term it's easier to stay as you are and look for the quick-fix 'external' answers found in the bottom of a meal replacement drink or a botox injection! Long term it's about listening and remembering our body's own dreams of being loved, nurtured, valued and held up with pride, regardless of our external appearance. Every **body** deserves to be loved and our souls long to be expressed through a body we adore.

Own Your Stone

Like the emergence of a beautiful sunrise you understand the message of the stones and realize that in order for you to move on to loving your body and feeling confident about you, you will need to name all of the body blocks you may have.

You know that you cannot go round, over or even underneath the stones – you have to go through them and on a spiritual level you know that once you have owned your stone you open up a pathway – a space for you to move through.

Name all your stones, writing on each one what it is about it that blocks, barricades or stops you from loving you. How do you prevent yourself from feeling fantastic and proud of your body? As you write on each one, mark that stone with a symbol. This can be anything you like – just make it something personal to you and that you will easily connect to and recognize. For example, a friend of mine always used to distract herself from doing the things she really wanted to do by cleaning, tidying, mending and generally continually making sure the house was in order. She felt that she couldn't move on and do all that she wanted until the washing up was done, the house vacuumed, the ironing finished and there was not a spot of dust left anywhere in the house. She named this as one of her stones and drew the symbol of a broom on the stone.

Another friend went to the gym every day of the week, spending about three hours on each session. She thought that she loved her body by doing this but this was, in fact, one of her biggest body blocks. As her workouts became more intense her body began to suffer from fatigue and sustained several injuries. Her home life began to creak at the knees, too, as she was never around long enough to enjoy being with her family. She realized she wasn't showing her body love but was punishing it instead. She named her workouts as one of her stones and her symbol was a pair of dumbbells.

Using the following as a template, name your stones and draw in your own symbols.

Own Your Stone

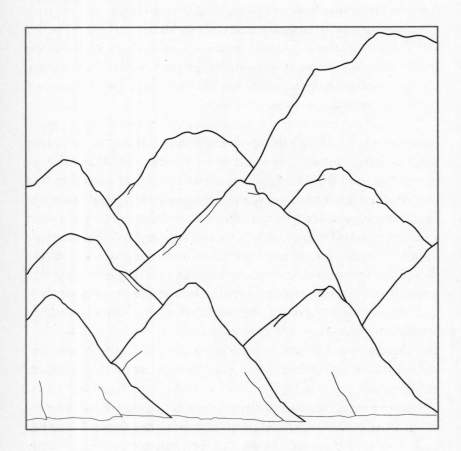

How Symbols Help you Recognize Your Body Blocks

In owning your stones and giving them a symbol you are connecting to the part of your subconscious that uses images to communicate with the conscious mind. Think of it as the mind's own short cut in communication. You can harness the power of the images you have selected by asking your subconscious mind to show you that

image every time you are about to self-sabotage or block yourself
in some way. My friend who uses cleaning as her number one
distraction now 'sees' the image of that broom every time she
begins to dust or tidy up. It reminds her not to become excessive
in her housework and to take time for herself. By linking the image
or symbol with the stone you can help clear your body barriers and
move through them. In essence, the symbols give you a mind/body
alert that you may be about to repeat an old pattern, or that you
need to stop and remember the journey you are on. Use the symbols
as your ultimate 'wake-up' call!

*As you name each stone and mark it with your symbol, the stones
begin to disappear one by one, sinking into the ground and opening
up a clear pathway for you to follow. Feeling the exhilaration of
being free from the rocks you had carried you begin to run the rest
of the way. Your body responds in an instant. Your heartbeat
increases and you are aware of the power in your legs as you push
yourself forwards. Breathing heavily now, you slow down a little
and notice that all the storm clouds have disappeared and all
around you is the smell of summer rain on the ground — earthy,
rich and intoxicating. You feel so alive as you walk powerfully
onwards. Your cheeks are flushed pink with life and every fibre
tingles with the joy of being you.*

*Just as you are about to leave Sabotage City, your attention is
caught by a peculiar whispering noise that seems to be coming from
underneath a small stone right in front of you. Peering a little closer
and wanting to leave no stone unturned, you lift up the stone to
reveal a brown, wizened little creature with a tiny golden hook
through one nostril. As you step back in surprise, the creature
wriggles his way out and introduces himself as Gomwart the helper.
Seeing the look of uncertainty on your face he continues to speak
quickly and tells you that he has brought you a gift — a protective
magical shield. He tells you that you must activate the shield by
writing the magic words of power on it — it will then help keep you
focused, positive and confident in all that you do.*

You thank him for his generosity and accept the huge golden circle which you place on the ground in front of you and begin to read the instructions.

The Victorious Circle

Create your own victorious circle by putting into action a loop of positive thoughts, feelings and actions that you can use to deal with any situation. Write at the top of the circle (Event/situation) what you want to deal with or need help with. Then go round the circle to the next section (New Thoughts/Beliefs). Write here the positive, uplifting thoughts you need to hold in your mind to help you overcome that particular situation. Continue round to the area marked 'Feelings'. Write here how you want to feel and make sure it is written in the present tense, ie 'I feel positive, energized and focused!' The final part asks you to identify your actions (action/behaviour). Write in the actions you need to take or behaviour you need to change to support your beliefs. You will then find yourself back at the top of the circle. As long as the situation at the top of the circle continues to be the same you need to keep repeating the steps you have just outlined.

In essence, you are building up a continuous ring of confidence as your thoughts affect your feelings, which in turn leads to a positive change in your behaviour or actions. The victorious circle can be used to help change any situation, worry or concern that you may have. The second diagram shows an example of someone working with low self-esteem.

> *As you leave Sabotage City way back in the distance you notice that you are now on a gradual slope. Sweeping upwards, the road curves round in a gentle arc and you wonder what lies around that bend. Within seconds you have turned the corner and in front of you, stretching upwards in folds of what looks like undulating green silk, is the most awesome mountain you have ever seen.*
>
> *You stop and absorb the majesty and power before you, feeling somehow that you are one with the mountain and that you too have this power coursing through your veins. Before you can wonder what*

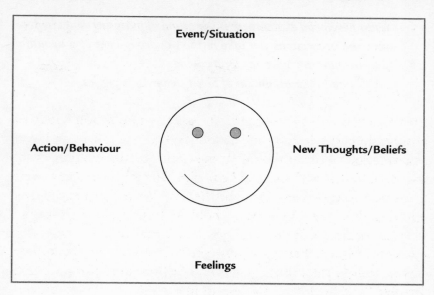

Draw your own victorious circle and activate the power of your protective shield.

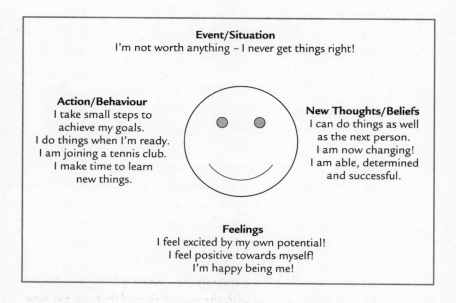

quest lies ahead of you there is the sound of fluttering wings by your side and you gasp as you take in the wondrous sight of a beautiful dancing butterfly hovering on the wind.

'Welcome to the Mountain of Self-Esteem,' she giggles.

6.
Climbing the Mountain
of Self-Esteem

As you gaze up at the Mountain of Self-Esteem you know instinctively that the next part of your quest is to climb it. As the butterfly softly kisses your cheek with her lilac gossamer wings, you know with all your being that you can do this. It feels like only yesterday when you took your first tentative steps into this magical land and now you're here, ready to climb this beautiful mountain — knowing that you'll get to the top!

Clarissa, the butterfly, flutters down onto your hand and allows the soft warm breeze to play air games with her wings.

'You are so beautiful,' you marvel as this glorious creature restores your belief in miracles.

Clarissa's voice whispers gently inside your head, 'There was a time when I grew a toughened skin around my body so I couldn't feel any more.'

'What happened?' you ask in your mind as she settles even more trustingly into your hand.

'I became what I was always destined to be — I became beautiful — just as you are.'

You feel a small temptation to say, 'But I'm not beautiful,' and then you stop — you remember your birth guardian's words, your symbols from the stones, your journey across the Sea of Change and your pledge to love yourself. Smiling at this exquisite fairy-like form, you say, 'Thank you — I believe I am!'

With that, you begin to walk towards the foot of the mountain. It's a perfect summer's day and you smile as a rabbit bobs and darts away, sniffing the air with an inquisitive nose — already sensing a whiff of autumn on its way. An exquisite gypsy caravan teeters by in the distance and a wispy pink cloud trails a lone star. As you begin your ascent, you notice that each step of the way is highlighted with markers pointing to the next level. The first marker you approach is a huge billboard with your face and name on it.

'Your first self-esteem task,' Clarissa whispers and flickers her way into the sky, gliding up and down over flowers and bushes as she disappears from view.

You look at the enormous billboard and feel shocked. You have never seen your image in so much detail before . . . and as you look closer you see the light in your eyes shining out pure happiness. Your smile radiates an inner bubble of joy and there is an aura of confidence all around you. You realize that you look so well, so alive, so very beautiful. And as you look deeper, you see things about you that you have never noticed before — warmth, peacefulness and a deep sense of belonging and pride.

You reach up and dreamily stroke your cheek — 'This is my skin, these are my eyes, my hair, my smile, my face — this is my name. This is me and there's not another like me in the world.'

Underneath the billboard is an empty space on which you are asked to write your own advertisement for yourself. It reads, 'Tell us who you are!'

Pump the Positive!

Begin by writing your name in capital letters at the top of a blank sheet of paper and then write out an advert telling the world who you are!

Tell the world what you want it to know – speak of your strengths, loves, passions and interests. Let the universe know about your journey and how far you've come, and what more you want to do, feel or experience.

Any advert gives us information about the product it is promoting. Imagine that **you** are the product and this advertisement is a message to all the people you have yet to meet or share your dreams with.

Create an Impact!

As in any advertisement, IMPACT COUNTS, and the first words you write need to grab your audience's attention.

Tell the world in your own words why you are special. Share what you can give and let us in to your hopes and dreams. Who are you? What makes you who you are?

Imagine that you have just been made chief marketing executive of a global advertising agency and the assignment this week is to relaunch you!

Your mission is to talk yourself up in the most positive terms and shine your light into the darkest recesses of this planet. Tell us what's new and different about you and how that affects your life and the lives of those around you. Tell us why we would love to be in your company and what unique talents, skills, gifts and beliefs you bring. Use any ideas, words or methods that you have discovered about yourself from the journey so far. Make the advert as long or as short as you like but make it come alive with the power of you! Pump the positive and begin to flex those mental muscles!

If you find it easier, rough it out before writing it in its finished form.

A Picture Speaks a Thousand Words

If you prefer, you could use pictures instead of words to create a visual image of how you see and promote yourself. Put a collage together of pictures that represent the very best about who you are and how you value yourself. Use magazines, brochures, etc and include any images that you love, or that make you feel loved, beautiful, empowered or reflect your dreams.

Take your time doing this – it's powerful stuff!

As you finish your advert you smile as your message of confidence shines out to the world – drawing wonderful new opportunities and experiences your way.

Clarissa is never far behind as you climb steadily upwards. The sun is deepening in its glory, dappling the world with gold as a double rainbow arcs its way overhead. Somewhere to your side a bumblebee buzzes from flower to flower.

'Life is good,' you sigh contentedly as you reach your next marker, which reads 'Plant a crop of dream visions!'

Clarissa reappears by your side and says, 'You've told the world who you are and showed us the beauty of you. It is now time to allow all your dreams to grow and flourish as you plant your tree of love.'

'What is the tree of love?' you ask quietly as Clarissa settles on your shoulder.

'The tree of love,' she sings, 'Is like the tree of life, only it is personal to you. It is made up of your body's dearest, most prized dreams.'

'I didn't know my body had dreams,' you answer in surprise.

'Oh yes — the body's dreams are the most powerful of all because they long to express your true spirit. They are usually stopped by a hurting or locked mind that says, "Don't be silly — you can't do that!" But the body knows better and the body's greatest dream is to be loved and cherished.'

She goes on — a little haltingly now. 'My body always knew it could fly but as a lowly caterpillar I didn't believe I could ever be anything else. I slowly crawled my way through life, trudging through a maze of endless green leaves — hunching, punching and munching with a bored kind of apathy until one day I got stuck in my cocoon.'

'What happened then?' you ask as Clarissa closes her wings sadly in remembrance of that day.

'I thought I was in prison and would never get out, although all of my friends hummed with excitement as they looked forward to the day that they would fly. All I felt was fear and disbelief that I could ever break free. Suddenly the sky was filled with the colour of sparkling wings — all my friends were free — all of them except me!'

You gently stroke her warm silky back as she continues, 'My best friend, Felicity, yelled at me, saying that she had had quite enough of my negative behaviour and told me to believe that I could do it — that it was possible for me to fly and be beautiful. She told me: "This is what you were born to be — we all are!" She got really *cross with me as she told me to see the beauty within myself and that I had to work at it – I had to want to change!*

'Well, I did and my beliefs set me free as I nibbled and pushed my way out of my bindings until first one wing was free, then another, until I was finally airborne.'

Clarissa suddenly soared into the blue beyond saying, 'Enough about me – this is your journey. Listen to your body's dreams; believe you can fly into a body you love with all your heart and soul.

Ask your mind to help, your spirit to lead you on and your body to dance the way home!'

And with that – she was gone.

The Body Gift Tree

This part of the Mountain of Self-Esteem asks you to plant your body's dreams so that they may take root and grow within your mind, body and soul.

Take a few moments to relax as deeply as you can. Breathe in fully through your nose for the count of three and then exhale through your mouth for four counts. Repeat this several times, feeling calm and centred.

When you are ready, ask your body to share its dreams with you as you answer the following questions. Each question asks a part of your body what its particular dream is – what it so longs for or loves to do. Each dream you discover is a gift – something that has the power to bring you pleasure and happiness as you connect with your body's innate inner wisdom and longing. Ask each part of your body what dreams it may have and then imagine that you are that body part. Imagine your body is speaking through you as it shares its innermost secrets.

Allow any images, senses, words or feelings to come up – even if they don't appear to make sense or have any meaning. Just write down your initial response to the question and look back at it later. Let your dreams pour forth and your imagination run wild and free. List all the things that come into your awareness, and if you are not aware of an answer immediately just move on to the next question and return to it later. Write your answers on each branch of the body tree (see the illustration on the opposite page), starting with the body part and then the dream it has. For example, I always love to wiggle my toes underneath the person sitting next to me (providing I know them of course!) so I would put against 'Toes' – 'Wiggle under friends! Comfort and warmth'. A friend adores the smell of air-dried clothes on a summer's day, so she wrote 'smells of summer' along the 'Nose' branch of the tree illustration. You can just write in the body dream or also include the feeling that goes along with this. It's up to you. Create your body gift tree as you choose it to be.

Let your body speak as you ask:

1 Where do your feet most long to walk?
2 What do your toes long to wiggle in?
3 Where do your legs dream of taking you?
4 What or who do your inner thighs most want to squeeze?
5 What are your buttocks' secret longings?
6 What dance do your hips long to groove to?
7 What does your colon so wish to clear?
8 What do your genitals dream of the most?
9 What does your stomach so want to feel?
10 What do your lungs desire to breathe in and out?
11 What does your heart crave to feel?
12 What are your breasts' deepest desires?
13 What do your shoulders yearn to carry?
14 What does your spine hanker after?
15 Who or what do your hands most love to touch or create?
16 What or who do your arms most want to hold?
17 What does your neck long to feel?
18 What does your throat want to swallow?
19 What words does your mouth long to say?
20 Who or what do your lips seek to kiss?
21 What do your teeth desire to bite?
22 What does your nose most desire to smell?

23 What sounds do your ears most yearn to hear?
24 What or who do your eyes most long to see?
25 How does your hair long to feel?
26 How does your skin aspire to feel?
27 What or who excites your mind?
28 What does your entire body crave to experience?

Take a while to review your answers, being aware of whether there are any questions that you find difficult to answer at the moment. Which answers just burst into life, and were there any that surprised, shocked, overjoyed or confused you?

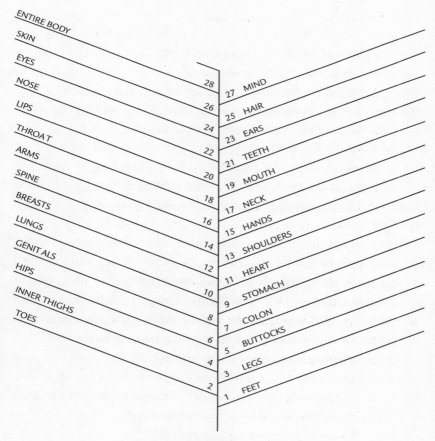

The Body Gift Tree

Just allow your body gift tree to filter through your being like roots reaching outwards into the soil, penetrating each and every part with its life force.

Getting Jiggy With it!

This body gift exercise calls you to contact and connect with each part of your body, allowing your body to speak to you of its long-held fantasies, desires and dreams. In writing out your body gift tree you focus on individual body areas which may previously have been ignored or forgotten about. How often do we ask our toes what they want to wiggle in or what sounds our ears ache to hear? We are usually so busy keeping strict tabs on our body (lest it do something it 'shouldn't') that we forget that our bodies need to play, move, jiggle, jump and express themselves in the fullest possible way. This exercise gives our body's dreams a chance to be heard. Some people may find this difficult to do, as we are so out of touch with focusing on just one part of ourselves in an open, questioning manner. If you found this hard to do it may be because the controlling part of your mind is stepping in, dictating how you 'should' respond and what you 'ought' to feel or dream. If this is the case, simply thank your mind for its input but reaffirm that you desire to become more aware of your body's messages.

Remember, your answers may come at a later time or make themselves known through dreams or even in moments of synchronicity in your life. You know those moments of apparent coincidence when everything falls into place as if by magic, and you meet the right people at the right time in the right place!

Writing this book was full of such moments and in the end I had to laugh, as whatever I had written about that day would usually appear some time later in symbols, pictures, magazines or television programmes! It's a fun game, as the more you affirm your own thoughts and beliefs, the more life smiles and affirms you – with a big 'thumbs up'!

Try to notice any patterns or themes in your answers and ask yourself if there is a connecting thread that ties all your dreams together.

Let's Get Physical!

The body gift exercise allowed you to connect with your body's dreams and fantasies. It's now time to connect with your body's feelings and self-expression as we play my version of 'Body Image Twister'!

This exercise will involve you getting up and actually doing the tasks given. Very often, our actions show us how we truly feel, more powerfully than words or thoughts. This exercise asks you to put your body in a shape that best expresses particular words and emotional states.

No matter how silly or foolish it may make you feel, try not to skip this part of the quest. Movement and dance therapy are often valuable ways in which to access the body's innermost feelings and release tension or pent-up emotions. Allow your body to make different shapes to express the words and, as you make the shape, hold the position for a few seconds as you fully experience and tune in to what your body is expressing. Become aware of where your body is holding tension, if your breathing changes and whether the shapes you make are free and expansive or closed and restricted. Is the shape symmetrical or asymmetrical? Notice as much as you can about the position and really be in it – holding it, breathing it, living it and allowing it to be. You can also gain great insight by doing this exercise with a friend. Whilst one of you makes the body shape, the other gives feedback about how that shape makes her/him feel and what she/he sees in it. Their feedback may not only give you a new perspective on how you see yourself but also about how your friend views him/herself. Only share this exercise if you are confident of a supportive, positive and loving environment in which you can feel free and safe enough to explore your body shapes.

Don't spend too long thinking about what shape you make – just do it and see what happens. Have fun!

Body Image Twister

Make a shape with your body, which expresses:

1	How you are right now	9	The present
2	Sadness	10	Peace
3	Freedom	11	Confidence
4	The past	12	Hope
5	Anxiety	13	Hate
6	Love	14	Sensuality
7	The future	15	Beauty
8	Joy	16	Balance

As always, take a few moments to evaluate the benefits of the exercise and experience, and how it made you feel. Were there any surprises, insights or feelings brought on by allowing your body this kind of physical expression? Remember, also, to note down if you chose not to do this and how that made you feel. Very often, the reasons we have for not doing something are as illuminating as the reasons for doing it.

The sun has turned into a vivid orb of voluptuous orange as it hangs low and full over the horizon, stretching out its long fingers of passion pink as it sets slowly into a powder-blue sky. A flock of silhouetted birds performs a highly choreographed flight display as they swoop, turn, dive and wheel around the top of the mountain, beckoning you on.

You begin to climb once more until, at last, you are standing on the very peak. As you gaze out the views expand forever and you have a deep spiritual feeling that you are one with the world around you. The air is thick with silence and you feel like a goddess surveying your kingdom. No one can touch you here and as you look out into the distance you know that you have left your past far behind. Everything is infused with a new perspective as you realize that climbing the mountain of self-esteem is a joy, and so much easier than you thought it was going to be.

One of the birds from the flight display team breaks free from its ranks and performs a flypast especially for you, dropping into your hands a small golden statue as it swoops by.

You look down and see that the golden figure is engraved with the words:

'Body Oscar Award'
For love, commitment, hard work, honesty, perseverance
and a deep connection to your uniqueness, spirit and all that
is you.

Suddenly the silence is broken by thunderous applause and, as you look around, all the people you have ever known in your life surround you, both dead and alive. Every one is there from your childhood to the present moment — smiling, clapping, cheering and delighted in your success — urging you on!

Every teacher, friend, colleague, passing stranger, lover, tormentor, uncle, aunt, sister, brother, mother, father. Everyone you have ever known or met, no matter how briefly, in your life is here supporting, loving, accepting and congratulating you for being exactly who you are!

Your nose feels a bit tingly and your eyes well up with emotion as a cry goes out from the rapturous throng below — 'Speech! Speech!' And then the entire crowd is clamouring and clapping harder and louder than ever.

'What do I say?' you ask no one in particular. Suddenly Clarissa is back by your side and you hear her voice inside your mind, 'Welcome to the Body Oscars — you have won the coveted Body Oscar award — it's now time for your acceptance speech!'

You step forward, your Body Oscar clasped firmly in your hand, and begin to speak. Your voice rings out over the mountain — clear, beautiful and strong. No one moves. They are all held captivated in your body confidence spell.

The Body Oscars

Imagine that you have been given the ultimate accolade – a prestigious award for loving your body, a Body Oscar. All those gathered around wait with baited breath for you to begin your acceptance speech.

In this speech, you need to thank all the different parts of your body for all the things they have done or given you throughout your life. Think of how your body has supported you or allowed you to achieve certain ambitions. Include times when your body has recovered after injury or illness to once again allow you to enjoy good health. What is it you want to thank your body for?

A friend of mine had always hated the stretch marks caused after the birth of her first child, but in writing her acceptance speech she thanked them for allowing her skin to stretch so her baby could grow. She said, 'I can't hate them now – they mark the most wonderful experience of my life!' Whatever you have gained, enjoyed, experienced or been privileged enough to do through your body – show your appreciation as you thank each and every fabulous part. This is an acceptance speech in the truest sense of the word. Your body, mind and spirit have brought you to where you are today – and today you're standing on top of the world giving thanks and being supported by your entire life. Wow!

Complete your Body Oscar speech here by filling in the blank spaces.

Acceptance Speech

I (write your name here) _____ am delighted to have been awarded the Body Oscar and would like to thank the parts of me that have made this all possible. Without you all, I would not be here today.

I would like to thank:

My legs for _____

My arms for _____

My thighs for _____

My hips for _____

My lungs for _____

My immune system for _____

My heart for _____

My calves for _____

My breasts for _____

My reproductive system for _____

My buttocks for _____

My skin for _____

My fingers for _____

My stomach for _____

My kidneys for _____

My ribs for _____

My wrists for _____

My spine for _____

My neck for _____

My ankles for _____

My hands for _____

My brain for _____

My fat for _____

My wrinkles for _____

My blood for _____

My genitals for _____

My scars for _____

My mouth for _____

My teeth for _____

My bones for _____

My muscles for _____

My toes for _____

My hair for _____

My ears for _____

And finally, I would like to thank my entire body, mind and spirit

for _____

As you finish your speech there is a moment of silence and then the audience explodes into life — cheering and clapping and basking in the glow of your reflected glory. And just as you feel that life can't get any better the crowd falls silent as the sound of beating wings fills the air. Landing softly beside you is the most beautiful magical creature you have ever seen. Part bird, part mythological being, and part pure fantasy. 'I am the Bird of the Present', it says as a big, roving, golden eye winks cheekily at you.

'Climb aboard my back and hold tight to my feathers and I will take you to lands yet unseen.'

You clamber up and nestle into the soft downy feathers and you feel warm, safe and loved as the bird soars into flight.

You snuggle down as the Mountain of Self-Esteem becomes a magical memory in your mind and you feel a deep warmth spread through your body.

On and on you fly until the velvet arms of the night fold you into her star-kissed embrace. On and on until morning calls out your name and a dusky moonbeam becomes tangled in your hair.

'You have earned your wings,' the Bird of the Present trills, as you fly on towards Here and Now Island.

7.

Here and Now Island

Your breath is taken away as you look down on what looks like an emerald jewel set in an expanse of glittering ice-blue diamonds. The bird banks gently to the left and then slowly begins his descent on to a golden spit of sand that stretches far out to sea.

You dismount, and the bird of the present lowers his beautiful proud head so that you can give him a hug goodbye. As you reach up and place your arms lovingly around his neck, he whispers softly in your ear, 'It's all here for you — every moment of every day. It's up to you what you create from this moment on. Stay in the present and know that your life is a gift — you have it all, live it well.'

Before you have time to reply, the bird fades away into the shimmering, shifting sands and you are left alone.

It's morning in paradise and the sun's heat gently arouses your skin and senses. You walk to the water's edge, allowing the warm, clear water to curl around your toes as it shrinks the sand from under your feet. Your progress is abruptly halted as you almost trip over a hard glass object that has found its way between your feet. You look down and see that it is a bottle with what looks like a message inside.

With a sense of curiosity, you pick it up and read the words etched into the glass, 'Message from your body!'

You think back to the day you wrote to your body as you prepared to cross the Sea of Change and know instantly that this must be the reply from your body. You smile as you break open the seal surrounding the top of the bottle and extract your body's message, which reads . . .

Message in a Bottle

This part of the journey is about resolution, completion and a coming together of all that you have experienced and worked through. It highlights awareness that, although the journey is near an end, there are always more adventures to be had, new places to explore and more beauty to behold. As one journey finishes a new one is already beginning, just as each day is like a 'mini' life – we constantly start each day anew with every sunrise. This journey is edging into the setting sun and tomorrow you'll awake recharged and feeling confident that you have the power to make each and every second count.

Take a few moments to fantasize about what your body would say to you – what message would your body give you? What is it you most need to hear and understand? What does your body dream of saying or expressing? Ask your body with a quiet voice in your mind what it would love to say to you. There's no restriction or constraint – your body is free to speak truly and you are open to listening without judgement, criticism or censorship in any way.

When you feel ready – write down your body's message on a separate sheet of paper. Make it as short or as long as you like. If you find that no message comes or that you feel unable to write anything at the moment – then write how you feel about **not** writing a message. Is it okay for you that you don't get the message in the bottle? How do you feel if you are unable to complete this part of the journey? Are there any other parts of the journey that you were unable to complete and do you notice any similarities? Write about what is going on for you.

It is important that your feelings are expressed in the 'here and now' and not allowed to become hidden away where their vital energy may become lost, stagnant, or end up as a stone around your neck or a weight on your shoulders. Stop the body blocks from forming by identifying and owning them as they arrive.

Love yourself enough to give yourself permission to express all that you feel. Remember that this is only about you. If you don't do it no one else will ever know – only you will, but you are the most important person of all.

Writing letters to and from your body is one way of creating a dialogue or communication between mind, body and spirit. As these three are intrinsically linked we already 'know' what is going on and how we are truly feeling in all of these areas – it's just hard to access this at times. The letter writing exercise may highlight certain feelings, thoughts or beliefs that you may have previously shut away or dismissed – even not being able to write a message is a message in itself.

Someone I once worked with said that she really didn't know what her body was doing any more – she was so out of touch with herself. Her husband had died three years earlier and since then she had been raising her two very energetic children. Friends had suggested that she could try dating again but when she looked in the mirror she just thought, 'Who am I? I don't know me – I can't imagine that anyone would ever be interested in a 48-year-old frumpy widow with two children and nothing to say for herself!'

However, imagination was just what she needed as she approached the letter writing exercise and tried to imagine what her body might say to her. She was shocked to find that her body's message was full of anger, hurt and accusations. Hidden underneath the anger was fear – fear of beginning again, of perhaps committing herself to another relationship, which may or may not last, or of seeing herself as an attractive woman and not just a mum. She had defended herself against hurt for so long that her body had begun to become invisible, almost as if it said, 'If you can't see me – you can't hurt me.'

Writing the body letter was a powerful and liberating experience. Before she began to write she had thought that there would be nothing to say and she was overwhelmed when her feelings poured out onto the paper. Gradually, over a period of about two months, she began to go out more and imagine herself as a confident, attractive woman in her own right. Her friends noticed a gentle change in her as she had her hair restyled to a softer, sexier image and updated her clothes to flatter her curvy figure.

Today, she is almost unrecognizable as the woman she was six months ago. It's not been easy for her and she has fought the changes every step of the way, often crying out tears of 'I can't do this – I don't want to do this!' But, she **has** done it and she loves herself mostly for not giving up on who she is. At the age of 48 her life has begun again and she's enjoying every minute of it.

As you read your message, a wonderful sense of peace settles like soft, cherry-blossom confetti within your body, mind and soul. You breathe in deeply the warm tropical air and gaze around you, feeding your body with the intense beauty of this magical island. The palm trees sway lazily and the sound of their swishing leaves lulls you into a deep, peaceful state of being – soothing and calming every part of you.

You walk over to where a hammock rocks invitingly – calling you to stretch out and relax in the cool dappled shade. Allowing one leg to dangle aimlessly over the side of the hammock you begin to fall into a dreamy meditation – not asleep, but not fully awake either. You allow your thoughts to drift away into eternal space and, as your breathing deepens, your muscles fully relax and feel heavy, warm and content. As your eyelids surrender to the lure of your inner visions and close sleepily, you smell the faint aroma of jasmine and the alluring sweetness of geranium. Sinking into deeper peace, you feel divinely guided by your inner essence.

Your dreams meander around your universe until something calls you to look to your side. A small movement focuses your attention on the most beautiful grey cat you have ever seen. He sits on the outstretched limb of an ancient tree bowed by passing storms, a gentle throb of a purr, like a distant tractor, rumbling through his whole body. There's a look of a distinguished old zen master about him as his white whiskers droop down the sides of his intelligent face. Something about this magnificent being tells you that he has more than outlived his allotted nine lives and is probably on life 4082! His eyes are like two neon blue spaceships – great orbs of translucent light reflecting huge saucers of wisdom – but as you stare more deeply, you realize that he is blind.

You hear the cat speak within your soul as he tells you that he is just one of your guides on this journey and that you will meet the others as you continue to travel. Until then he would love to see what you look like and asks you to describe yourself. But, being a cat (and a magical one at that), he needs you to answer in the universal language of all metaphysical dream beings — the language of images and symbols. You agree to do so and relax as he purrs out his first question . . .

If Your Body Was a . . .

This exercise is a revamp of the popular psychological party game, 'If you were an animal, what animal would you be?' It calls you to respond intuitively and quickly to a series of questions designed to build up an entire picture of your body image, awareness and perception. Don't think too hard about your answers — go with whatever comes, have fun and let go!

1 If your body was a colour, what colour would it be?
2 If your body was a building, what kind of building would it be?
3 If your body was an article of clothing, what would it be?
4 If your body was an emotion, what emotion would it be?
5 If your body was an age, what age would it be?
6 If your body was a shape, what shape would it be?
7 If your body was a material, what material would it be?
8 If your body was a temperature, what temperature would it be?
9 If your body was a song, what song would it be?
10 If your body was a book, what book would it be?
11 If your body was a country, what country would it be?
12 If your body was a liquid, what liquid would it be?
13 If your body was a food, what food would it be?
14 If your body was a dance, what dance would it be?
15 If your body was a precious jewel, what jewel would it be?
16 If your body could speak, what would it say?

Read back through your answers and just become aware of the 'feel' they give you. When I first did this exercise I created an amusing visual image of a lilac-blue furry, round hot boat travelling through milk aged about four, crying out, 'Help – Love me!'

Every time I have done this since, I have experienced ever-changing answers depending on how I am at that point in time. It's a lighthearted game and one that can be shared with friends if you wish. But, be aware that although your answers may be amusing, strange or just incomprehensible – they do give powerful clues as to how you see your body. Very often words only give us half of the whole picture. By incorporating a visual stimulus we can often see things in ourselves that we may have missed or disregarded before.

Allow the answers to play in your subconscious – don't be tempted to overanalyse or look too deep. There is no right or wrong way to respond to this game and the results are only relevant to you. It's what **you** make of the meaning that counts. Someone else's interpretation could be totally wrong. Trust your feelings and let your images bring you insight. My own rather peculiar image made perfect sense to me at the time although my friends howled with laughter when I shared this with them, as they could not understand it at all!

The grey one jumps down effortlessly on to the sand, where he rolls over on his back, waiting for his tummy to be kissed. You do so obligingly and he thanks you for sharing your beauty with him.

Tail held high and whiskers on the alert, he prowls possessively towards the sea where he jumps up onto a rock to sunbathe.

'You'd never know he was blind,' you think to yourself as an ethereal chanting sound to your left catches your attention.

Turning your attention away from the cat you listen for the sound again. It's beautiful – like crystal bells, Tibetan bowls and children's laughter all rolled into one haunting, spine-tingling melody. The hairs on your arms stand on end as your skin breaks into little bumps of soul pleasure.

Far out to sea you spot the source of the sound as seven satiny, slate-grey dolphins arc their way in and out of the water, singing their 'soul mantra' as they dip and dive. You feel so privileged and overwhelmed with emotion as you watch this enchanting sight. And then, almost unbelievably, the dolphins turn towards you and call you to come into the water. Without hesitation you run towards the beckoning blue sea and plunge your body deep into the warm, welcoming waves. You know that you are totally safe as these seven beautiful beings surround you.

Two of them circle behind you and push their firm noses into the soles of your feet. Another two swim along either side of you and you hold on to their fins gently. The final three lead the way and with a high-pitched sonic whoop of joy they take off — carrying you with them. You feel like you are flying as your body is propelled just above the water by these spectacular creatures.

You feel exhilarated as they begin to slow down, and you find yourself climbing onto a small flat rock in the middle of the sea. As your skin dries in the warmth of the sun one of the dolphins begins to speak, telling you that it is time for you to choose a 'Body Mantra'.

You ask what this is as you have never heard of this before and the dolphin who calls herself Trottalina explains . . .

'A body mantra is your own special symbol and word to help you in your quest. Whenever you feel low or a bit frustrated, depressed or unsure — use your body mantra to help you focus your energies. It's like an instant "pick me up" and reminds you that you are lovely, special, beautiful and worth working for.'

You laugh as Trottalina flips on her back and smiles her brilliant dolphin smile, waving a flipper in the air in a rather queenly manner.

'How do I find my body mantra?' you ask as Trottalina rolls over and over just for the sheer fun of it.

'We've found them for you — all you have to do is select one of the symbols and then choose one of the words to go with it. It's easy! Just choose the first image that calls or jumps out at you from the page and then select the word that you feel will give you what you need. Put them together and, voila, you have your own unique body mantra.'

'Do you have one?' you ask curiously.

Trottalina performs a 'high five' sky leap as she answers, 'Of course — but ours tells other people how beautiful we are. We already know it!'

And with that, all the dolphins circle you protectively as you climb aboard Trottalina's broad shiny back and you are carried safely to the shore.

Body Mantras

A body mantra is something I have designed to help keep you focused or centred on what you want. Just as people use affirmations or visualizations to help keep them aware and 'on track', body mantras will help you to connect your body, mind, spirit and emotions in your own unique quest for body love and confidence.

Body mantras are a universal language of the subconscious mind. Meditate on the symbol you choose and link it with your word, creating your own personal body mantra.

Words or images are symbolic when they imply something more than their obvious and immediate meaning. They have a wider 'unconscious' aspect that is never precisely defined or fully explained. For example, our dreams sometimes contain elaborate or picturesque fantasies that can be deciphered according to what those images represent. A friend of mine recently dreamt of a beautiful chestnut horse, which was tied upside down and left hanging at the end of her garden. Deeply disturbed by this image she investigated further and found that the horse represented freedom and playfulness. As it was tied upside down, this meant to her that she needed to have some more fun in her life.

Carl G Jung, the psychologist, formulated a concept that all images could be reduced to certain basic patterns, which he called 'the collective unconscious'. This contains images that have been used for thousands of years and have a subconscious response in our minds, just as a biologist or anatomist finds many traces of original patterns in our bodies – for example, the human foetus resembles those of other animals.

So, too, has the psyche developed, storing images which we may only access within our dreams or other meditative, free-thinking states. Jung termed these 'archetypal images'.

By harnessing the power of these ancient and universal images, we can connect with our subconscious mind, asking it to aid and work with us in our quest for total body confidence and love. By adding a word to the image, the power is intensified and by keeping this symbol in our thoughts we have a unique tool to keep us focused, aware and living in the 'now'!

Select Your Body Mantra

Select a symbol – what are you most drawn towards? Go with the first image that appealed to you or attracted you instantly. Then turn to the following pages and choose a word or words connected with the particular image you have chosen. Try not to choose many words, as it is best to keep your body mantra simple and easy to remember. (Do not read the associated words until you have chosen your image.)

The Winged Heart – Associated Words

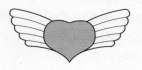

* Divine guidance
* Inspiration
* Spiritual frequencies
* Free to love
* Transcendence
* Swiftness
* Courage
* Joy
* Devotion
* Openness

* Love that is carried
* Success in whatever is important to you
* Heart set free
* Combined effort
* Raising of consciousness
* Giving and receiving love

* Wisdom
* Divine protection
* Feeling
* Victory
* Understanding
* Flight

The Cat (Bast) – Associated Words

* Desire
* Liberty
* Transformation
* Peace
* Knowledge
* Love
* Awareness
* Flexibility
* Individuality
* Grace
* Beauty
* Intuition
* Independence

* Relaxation
* Mental integration
* Balance
* Protection
* Maternal love and nurturing
* Sensuous
* Mystical

Sirius (The Sacred Star of the Ancients) – Associated Words

* Adventure
* Seeker of the great mysteries of the universe
* Coordinated effort – mind, body and spirit
* Shine
* Guide
* Eternal
* Hope
* Destiny

* Strength through prayer, meditation, spiritual awareness
* Belief in the universe
* Physical stamina

* Cosmic roots
* Athlete
* Pioneer
* Explorer

* Education
* The highest attainment
* Light
* Love

The Eye (of Horus) – Associated Words

* Healing energy
* Mind power
* The sun
* Divine insight
* Love
* Opening
* Spiritual perception

* Physical energies harnessed by power of the mind
* Strength
* Watchfulness
* Wisdom
* Enlightenment
* Stability
* Illumination
* Protection

The Lotus Flower – Associated Words

* Continuity
* Calmness
* Relaxation
* Confidence in your self
* Inner peace
* Seek the self
* Connections

* Blossom
* Grow
* Stillness
* Beauty
* Creation
* Resurrection
* Rebirth
* Purity
* Unfolding of the heart
* Support
* Past, present and future
* Spiritual unfolding
* Love

If you liked the cat image best and selected one of the cat's words, for example, 'balance', you have put together your own body mantra – the image of the cat with the word balance. This can now be used as a powerful symbol for you to use in meditations, visualizations or just when you need to feel more centred, focused or balanced in your life.

I use my own body mantra whenever I am feeling particularly stressed and find that just concentrating on the symbol and word brings me into a calmer state of being. All worries come in second place as I reaffirm what it is I need in my life and how I desire to feel. Sometimes I find myself just doodling or drawing the symbol, which once again helps me to remember the journey I am on and how I desire to feel and be.

The quest for body confidence is hard enough as it is, and every day brings a choice of how you are going to think, respond, act and treat your body. Some days are better than others and that's where having a body mantra helps – it just gives you an edge, a focus – something to help you connect and remember that life's too short to spend it not liking, loving or feeling confident about who you are.

The Chalice

With your body mantra firmly in your mind, you wave to the dolphins as they perform one last sky leap and plummet into the water, disappearing underneath bubbles of foamy froth as they torpedo their way out to sea.

The sun is less intense now and as the twilight deepens you are drawn towards a pathway lit by candles. You feel a deep sense of peace and acceptance as the flickering lights guide you to the entrance of an exquisite crystalline cave. Glistening deep within the rocks are diamonds, rose quartz, aquamarine, topaz, moonstones and many other precious and semi-precious stones.

As you peep inside the entrance you notice that straight ahead of you is a magnificent white marble table with the most beautiful fine crystal chalice standing elegantly in its centre.

As you draw closer, you notice a silver envelope with your name on it. You open it and read the following note:

'Congratulations on all that you have achieved on your journey so far. You now stand before your last challenge. You are requested to make your own body magic potion — an elixir of love, acceptance and strength. This is for your consumption alone. Below are a list of ingredients and a recipe for you to follow as you select the items to create your potion. Weave your own body magic together, drink deep of your unique energies and enjoy your journey home.'

The Body Magic Potion

Listed below are a wealth of 'ingredients' you can choose from to create your own particular brand of magic. Choose the words which you find most inspiring, stimulating, confidence making, or which evoke certain feelings. The recipe is given below — all you need to do is fill in the blank spaces with the appropriate words you have chosen. Remember that as you work your magic, what you think and believe about yourself will become true for you. Make your potion your own elixir of total confidence and love for who you are.

You may also select any other words which are not on the list, but which you want to include in your potion. Remember, these words embody how you want to feel. They are the energy behind the action — the motivation behind the movement.

Ingredients
Love ★ Positivity ★ Energy ★ Power ★ Self-belief ★
Creativity ★ Awareness ★ Connectedness ★ Laughter ★
Joy ★ Self-worth ★ Confidence ★ Vibrancy ★ Gracefulness ★
Harmony ★ Self-respect ★ Happiness ★ Inner strength ★
Wisdom ★ Healing energy ★ Freedom ★ Light ★
Compassion ★ Fun ★ Pleasure ★ Honesty ★ Self-truth ★
Divine guidance ★ Inspiration ★ Faith ★ Self-acceptance ★
Empathy ★ Self-esteem ★ Excitement ★ Passion ★

Enthusiasm ★ Kindness ★ Openness ★ Willingness ★ Sensuality

Body Magic Potion Recipe
Candle shining in the night
May my thoughts of love be planted
As I mix my potion of love
May my body confidence be granted

Place your bowl of life before you. Take two large helpings of _____ and mix together well. Sprinkle in a dash of _____ plus a slice of _____. Add in a touch of _____ and blend together with huge quantities of _____. Finally, stir in _____ with sunshine, and whisk the flowing energy of _____ into your completed mix. Blend together and serve daily as an invigorating tonic for mind, body and soul.

Look at the words you have chosen for your potion. Make them an everyday part of your life. Integrate them in all that you do.

All through this journey you have been asked to select words which will empower you and define how you wish to feel, act, think and believe. Remember, the words that you use about yourself are immensely powerful. Just as words written in a book or acted out in a film have the power to move you to laughter or tears, the words you use about you have the power to transform, transcend and transport you into feeling fantastic about you.

Look at how communication has grown and boomed over the years. It wasn't so long ago that only the very elite had mobile phones – now children have them as a normal part of their lives.

Whilst technology has gone on to increase our communication across the world, through the internet, telephone conferencing, email, etc, our own internal communication has diminished, leaving us more out of touch with our selves than ever before. As science pulls us forever onwards, no one has yet invented a way that you can keep in touch with your self. Only **you** can do that – only **you** can keep the lines free and the connection clear and open with your self. Every time we get caught up by distractions or become slaves to the 'should' master – every time we dull our senses with too much food, alcohol, work, cigarettes, negative thinking or through just not having enough fun – the lines become clogged and we end up getting a 'busy' signal or, even worse, a shrill unobtainable tone!

I Can See the Lights of Home

The journey you have just been on is one way of making sure that your call is always answered. It asks your dreams, thoughts, imagination, beliefs, faith, trust and sense of fun to connect with the whole of you – on every level.

As you continue on your way, stay connected and in love with this extraordinary thing called life. Communicate your dreams, fears, wishes, desires, thoughts, talents, concerns, hopes and ideas. Remember that the positive uplifting words you say today may inspire others to look at their lives or their bodies differently. An idea you may be keeping safely squirreled away may be the launching pad for a rocket full of promises. The way you smile and accept your rounded hips, off-centre nose, or bony shoulders may show your children that it's okay to feel safe in their own bodies. Pass it on and make your legacy one of confidence, love, peace and a tremendous passion for living!

Communicate who you are in all that you do, but mostly communicate the love, self-belief and respect you have for your home in this lifetime – your body.

As night weaves her seductive spell of darkness into the cave, the flames of the candles burn brighter than ever. Your intuition lures you towards the chalice and you pour in your body magic potion. The glass seems to fill up with tiny crystals of sparkling, dancing light. You stand back in awe watching this energy flow into the cave like a bejewelled waterfall, cascading its rainbow droplets over all that it touches. Everything seems alive with light as the crystals glimmer and shimmer, throwing healing energy into every corner of the cave. And then, you hear the sound – quiet at first but becoming louder as a soft tropical rain patters its way into the cave.

'Drink me,' the raindrops seem to say.

As the rain pours down with more intensity, you hear the insistent tap-tapping cry, 'Drink me, drink me, drink me!'

Smiling, you lift the crystal chalice to your lips and drink deep of the body magic you have created.

Swallowing the pure energy of your words, you feel their power being absorbed into every part of your being and become you.

Feeling almost drunk on your desire you take in every last drop. And finally, feeling satisfied and content, you look up in surprise to where a huge, ornate mirror has magically appeared in front of you. As you see your reflected image in the clear glass, the mirror speaks softly to you, urging you to applaud yourself.

'Go on,' she sings, 'You know you want to!'

You stand and look deeply at your reflection as if you are seeing yourself for the first time and then gently and quietly you put your hands together and begin to clap. Slow and unsure at first as the sound echoes around the cave, but gradually becoming louder, stronger and more enthusiastic, you applaud your energy, commitment, strength, determination, openness, willingness, creativity and incredible confidence and beauty. You hear a voice cry out, 'Bravo!' and look around in surprise before realizing that it was you!

As the sound of your applause resounds around the world you suddenly wonder how you are going to get home. Then the thought hits you: 'You are home – when you love yourself you are always home!'

Final Exercise

You know what I'm going to say – yep, here it is! The ultimate quest!

Stand in front of a mirror and applaud you! No big deal – you either do it or you don't. Only **you** know – only **you** will ever know! But then, this is only about **you**!

Bibliography

Ashley, N, *Create Your Own Reality: A Seth Workbook*, Prentice Hall Press, 1987.

Causton, R, *Nichiren Shoshu Buddhism*, Rider, 1988.

Chopra, D, *Unconditional Life*, Bantam, 1992.

Cooper, JC, *An Illustrated Encyclopaedia of Traditional Symbols*, Thames and Hudson, 1988.

Craze, R, *Feng Shui for Beginners*, (Headway) Hodder and Stoughton, 1994.

De Mello, A, *Awareness*, Fount, 1997.

Gawain, S, *Creative Visualization*, Bantam, 1985.

Glouberman, D, *Life Choices and Life Changes Through Imagework*, Aquarian, 1992.

Gurdjieff, GI, *Views From the Real World*, Routledge and Kegan Paul, 1979.

Hay, L, *Love Your Body*, Edengrove Editions, 1990.

Hay, L, *You Can Heal Your Life*, Edengrove Editions, 1988.

Hope, M, *The Book of Talimantras*, Thoth Publications, 1986.

Hutchinson, MG, *Transforming Body Image*, The Crossing Press, 1985.

Jeffers, S, *Feel the fear and do it anyway*, Arrow, 1987.

Johnson, S, *The Precious Present*, Doubleday, 1992.

Jung, CJ, *Man and his Symbols*, Aldus Books Ltd, 1964.

Kingston, K, *Creating Sacred Space with Feng Shui*, Piatkus, 1996.

Levoy, G, *Callings: Finding and Following an Authentic Life*, Thorsons, 1998.

Lidell, L, *The Sensual Body*, Guild Publishing, 1987.

Mackewn, J, *Developing Gestalt Counselling*, Sage Publications, 1999.

Maltz, M, *The Magic Power of Self-Image Psychology*, Reward Classics, 1964.

Maltz, M, *Psycho-Cybernetics*, Prentice Hall, 1960.

Markham, U, *Creating a Positive Self-Image*, Element, 1995.

McFarland, D, *Body Secrets*, Healing Arts Press, 1988.

McWilliams, P and Roger, J, *Do It!*, Thorsons, 1992.

McWilliams, P and Roger, J, *You Can't Afford the Luxury of a Negative Thought*, Thorsons, 1991.

Miller, EE, *Software for the Mind*, Celestial Arts, 1987.

Miln Smith, D, and Leicester, S, *Hug the Monster*, Rider Books, 1996.

Norfolk, D, *Think Well, Feel Great*, Michael Joseph, 1990.

Palladino, CD, *Developing Self-Esteem*, Kogan Page Ltd, 1990.

Perls, F, Hefferline, RF, Goodman, P, *Gestalt Therapy*, Souvenir Press, 1998.

Powter, S, *Stop the Insanity*, Orion, 1995.

Ray, S, *The Only Diet There is*, Celestial Arts, 1981.

Robbins, A, *Awaken the Giant Within*, Simon and Schuster, 1991.

Robbins, A, *Unlimited Power*, Simon and Schuster, 1986.

Robinson, S and Corbett, T, *The Dreamer's Dictionary*, Grafton Books 1988.

Rodin, J, *Body Traps*, Vermilion, 1992.

Rogers, CR, *On Becoming a Person*, Constable, 1996.

Rowan, J, *The Transpersonal*, Routledge, 1998.

Shapiro, D, *The BodyMind Workbook*, Element, 1990.

Viorst, J, *Necessary Losses*, Fawcett Gold Medal, 1986.

Wegscheider-Cruse, S, *Learning to Love Yourself*, Health Communications Inc, 1987.

Wilde, S, *The Quickening*, White Dove International Inc, 1998.

Williamson, M, *A Return to Love*, HarperCollins, 1996.

Williamson, M, *A Woman's Worth*, Rider, 1993.

Williams, M, *The Velveteen Rabbit*, Puffin Books, 1986.

Wolf, N, *The Beauty Myth*, Doubleday & Company, 1992.